A Natural
Farming System For
Sustainable Agriculture
In the Tropics

By Keith O. Mikkelson

A Natural Farming System for Sustainable Agriculture in the Tropics

Using EM or EM1® (Effective Micro-organisms).

Used as a Training Manual for a Sustainable Agriculture Course

Seminars: Saturdays 8:00 AM

Consultation: Mondays - Saturdays by Appointment

Advanced Training: by Appointment

1st Printing – 2000 pcs.

2nd Printing – 2000 pcs.

2005 Keith O. Mikkelson

ISBN 971-93381-0-5

PUBLISHED IN THE PHILIPPINES BY ALOHA HOUSE INC.

Mitra Rd., Santa Monica, Puerto Princesa City

5300 Palawan, PHILIPPINES

Tel. No. (0063) 48-434-6011 / 434-7837

TelFax: 434-6843

E-Mail: mik@mozcom.com

Website: www.alohahouse.org

Keith O. Mikkelson

Founder / Executive Director

Dedicated to
all the Tropical Natural Farmers,
like Andry Lim and Simon Gill, who taught
me the benefits of growing food naturally.

And to my Grandfather, Orlando Mikkelson, who tilled the earth in
Wisconsin just as his Norwegian immigrant parents did before him.

And to the contemporary authors like Elliot Coleman
and John Jeavons, who showed me through
print how to do it profitably.

My family started with draft horses. Later my grandfather converted a car into the family tractor and used it to work the land in Wisconsin.

Simon Gill and Andry Lim (right) mix up a brew of Fermented Plant Extracts.

Simon Gill, Director of Bountiful Harvest, left, and the author team-teach on the proper use of beneficial microorganisms in the tropical farmscape. Aloha House has trained over 1,000 farmers and gardeners on natural methods of food production.

Acknowledgement

I would like to acknowledge those individuals who read various manuscripts and gave helpful advice that made this book more than what I could have done on my own. Annacar Billano helped with spelling, grammar and publishing. Dr. Suzanne Evangelista gave my English the polish that only a professor in literature could. Simon Gill was helpful as a horticulturist. Both Simon Gill and Dave Blowers gave me the British and American perspectives as it relates in an Asian context.

My wife patiently edited and gave salient points to improve the format as well as inspire the cover layout. She is an inspiration to me and a blessing to her people.

It is the Creator Himself, the Lord Jesus Christ, whom I acknowledge as the One who holds the universe in His hand. He gives man insight into the creation in order to produce healthy food products that keep His servants effective in the Kingdom.

Preface

This book is an important work for tropical agriculture. There are very few resources that are truly "organic" and practical for the everyday farmer in the tropical setting. This book covers material that is extremely useful for the day-to-day operation of a farm or garden. It contains planning material that takes into account logistics as well as timetables.

This is not a guide for the agronomy student. I have identified several species that work well for us, but I do not have a planting guide for rice or corn or vegetables. These guides are readily obtained from seed suppliers and general horticultural works. If the reader looks carefully, he will find that I have given a system for natural fertilization in place of the chemical recommendations by traditional methods. Some creative adaptation will be required if your conditions and climate vary. We have a high acid clay soil that was rainforest at one time. Over the years a cogon grass has established itself. That is our starting point and our formulas can be changed for particular challenges that the reader may be facing.

This is not a How-to-do-it manual. Rather, this is a HOW-WE-DO-IT book based on my "Sustainable Agriculture in the Tropics" manual. It has been used to train and equip hundreds of small-scale farmers and gardeners in the natural farming adventure. It is an adventure worth taking, as few things in life will improve general health and well being as much as quality food products grown to their full potential.

Keith O. Mikkelson – Fall 2005

CONTENTS

Butterflies are commonplace in the natural farm.

DVD Video

A Natural Farming System

Sustainable Agriculture

In the Tropics

by Keith O. Mikkelson

DVD Training - Be sure to visit our on-line video store for more great training, featuring the hands on and lecture phases of our sustainable agriculture program for farmers and gardeners. See the videos at CustomFlix:

Course One
http://www.CustomFlix.com/207585

Course Two
http://www.CustomFlix.com/207646

My wife, Narcy, poses with our 4+kilo papaya "world champion", raised in only 20 liters of fermented kitchen garbage made with 12¢ US (6 pesos) of bokashi

Introduction

W hen you live in the developing world, you start to see things differently. I started visiting this country on short-term visits with Christian groups in 1995. I surveyed the rural areas and worked with people who were trying to make a difference with the knowledge they had. It's hard to ignore some of the problems that are emerging on our near horizon, but of course a local community is painfully aware of its own problems. It was sobering to see first hand, the struggle people endure to survive within the rural farming system. Entire food growing communities are nominalized due to the high cost of production. Chemical fertilizers have increased four-fold since I moved here in 1998. The lowland farmers have no heritage to pass on to their children. The old system of slash and burn, shifting cultivation is no longer sustainable due to encroaching development and outside pressures. The tribal groups practicing this technique have little to show for their efforts.

The nursery and green house are peaceful sanctuaries at Aloha House.

Living in the West, I was prone to the filters and biases that had kept me from the full reality of what was happening on a global scale. I could always live in a subdivision to my liking, buy a car of my choice on terms appropriate for my credit risk, and shop in the stores that I could afford. I could always avoid the *bad* neighborhoods or change channels on my television if the news was too worrisome. Therefore, I was well insulated from the poverty that grips the developing world.

As I began to travel in Asia, I was impressed by the expanse, and the potential, despite the poverty. Everywhere you go you see the poor. You can't escape it. You can't avoid the overcrowding in the cities, with thousands of beggars and homeless people. In the rural areas it's no better. I now realize that these are still agrarian societies. Half of the population has been sold the false hope of making it in the big cities, but it never works out the way they were promised. These groups of hopefuls have little to offer the urban work force; whatever work they can find to do is usually for the lowest wages allowed. Without a viable skill set to offer employers, they quickly become statistics. They just cannot cope. Many urban squatters have land out in the provinces, but they can no longer use it. They cannot afford to farm; the family property is sitting idle.

Out in the countryside, there are still some farmers holding on, looking for something that will pay the bills. They are continuing on in the noble duty of supplying food for others. This used to be a time-honored profession. However, times are changing. Issues are inter-related like never before. The technology used by small hold farmers is either too modern to be of any practical use or too old to be effective. Yet this is a time for rational optimism and discerning action.

The Mayor's project: the Puerto Princesa City sanitary landfill. It will soon be operational. 50% of city waste is organic material. It can be made into compost.

I believe there will always be the poor on this planet, till the Creator sets things right. I am not proposing any kind of a revolution, nor a political transformation. I am presenting a compendium of valuable technologies and techniques that can empower the food producers on this green planet to succeed; implemented at whatever level they are at; from backyard gardeners to American plantations to tropical agro-forestry.

There is nothing new here that hasn't been said better elsewhere, except for my own personal experience and perspective. This is a compilation of techniques that are useful for us, a small orphanage located on an organic farm in Palawan. However, the principles are well thought out and can be adapted to the readers' needs. The technology I have utilized is being used on a large scale as well as a small scale, from a tropical climate to arid conditions. The techniques can be gleaned from a dozen sources, but this is perhaps the most concise way to communicate them. In addition, the advantages are many.

When a family takes on gardening, it gains a new awareness of the world they live in. Most people are so disconnected from their nutritional inputs that they can't fathom the value in fresh food till they grow it. Even large-scale farmers sell tons of corn or soy and still have to shop at a supermarket to get their meals. When a family is planting and harvesting together, a growing appreciation for fresh, high quality produce, naturally sweet fruits and the life cycle of a plant emerges. They become preparation participants in their diet. They get connected to their food supply again.

Chronicled in these pages are my own insights; personal lessons as I journeyed through the adventure of learning to grow high

quality food. As executive director of Aloha House, I can testify, first hand, the effect these home grown foods have on our clients. My wife Narcy and I oversee the children's home and orphanage. We rescue children from tough situations.

They need high quality fruits and vegetables to build them back up. We have seen some of the sickest of children respond to fresh

carrot juice, vine ripened tomatoes, papaya, wheat grass, and blendered salads with lettuce, spinach, cucumbers, tomatoes etc. It is truly amazing how God has designed the body to respond to proper nutrition. These children are a real blessing and we are glad we can place them into permanent families. When they come, most

Often the children come sickly or under nourished. This child arrived at 2 years old and was dangerously malnourished.

of them cannot smile and are very insecure.

We had a girl come to us malnourished and sickly. With proper medical supervision, medication and good nutrition the pictured child (left) recovered. She was given carrot juice 3 times per day and ate the best fresh foods we could grow. A wonderful Christian couple has adopted her and she continues to grow and is secure in her new family.

This is one of the reasons we grow nutritious food. The children in our care are in need of that extra level of care due to the lack of pre-natal care from their birthmothers. It is always amazing to see the way God has designed the human body to repair itself through proper nutrition.

Fresh carrot juice - this little girl was surrendered for adoption. Because of the neglect of basic care, she was malnourished and had both T.B. and pneumonia. Good food and good doctors can really make a difference.

Prior to moving to the Philippines to start an orphanage, I worked for 15 years as a professional sports instructor. I had no agricultural training. I just read as much as possible. There is a huge volume of reliable information out there. I also attended seminars from progressive Filipinos promoting organic practices. There are a growing number of citizens wanting to succeed at organic production.

Simon Gill and Andry Lim (Right). Andry is still actively teaching technology from Korea. I was able to attend one of his early seminars in Palawan. The microbial production system is suited for hands on people who want to culture their own microbes from scratch. Raw sugar is used instead of molasses. Now he's also promoting good soil management practices throughout the provinces.

When we started achieving measurable success, community members were interested in learning the secrets of composting, organic farming and microbial inoculation. I read as much as I could get my hands on and visited farms when we traveled. I then began teaching these techniques to those people who wanted reliable information, right here on our small farm. We have various groups coming from the entire province now, eager to reduce fertilizer costs or control insects.

Some of our students are just starting out, others are already farming or gardening. We get all kinds of people. We've had the Peace Corps, PICARRT, IDEAS, El Nido Foundation, City councils,

Provincial board members, a deaf school, city / municipal departments, Dept. of Agriculture, and college groups join our training programs.

We are a duly Accredited Welfare Agency with the Department of Social Welfare and Development. We started as an orphanage to help needy children. We learned to help the mothers by offering training in sewing, card making etc. We offered livelihood as a means of providing for their children. Now we help families as well as children, in the hopes that they won't have to abandon or neglect their sons and daughters. Some of them lack opportunity. We give them the chance they are hoping for, but only if they are willing to work for it. For example, our Mothers with Hope Program is for women in crisis pregnancy. They get a chance to earn while they learn. Some take on food sales and agriculture.

These babies are healthier than those fed the standard American diet. No Gerber products here. We give them as much fresh fruits, vegetables, grains and legumes from the farm as they can eat.

Growing food is a good livelihood for the mom at home raising her children. There is a special sense of satisfaction when you create delicious meals from your own produce. You know it is a healthy meal and family can appreciate the great recipes that come from

Feeding time for the children is a happy time. They eat fruits and vegetables from the farm.

cooking your own food.

Hungry onlookers who appreciate high quality home made dishes eagerly anticipate this batch of Filipino style Korean Kimchi.

Korean style Kimchi is a favorite, with radish, onion, garlic and Pechay, all from the garden. We grow 3 different chili varieties we use for various Thai and Indian dishes. We also grow the curry plant for the leaves, they add seasoning to our curry recipes at home. Indian coriander is another exotic herb we grow for our Vietnamese dishes.

Government subsidized rice can be a thing of the past when each family learns to grow their own food.

So now I make my little contribution to the greater established works, in the hopes that it can benefit more farmers and families looking for a high quality of life. Whoever will listen can learn. Some will learn more than others, but I assure you, there is something in here for anyone looking for natural solutions to our man made, un-natural problems.

Big papaya, big head - The author has lots of big ideas when it comes to agriculture, health, nutrition and life in general. He takes on a creation assumption, asserting that the reader has already come to the obvious conclusion that the Creator has set forth a signature in His work, both in the planet earth and in mankind.

Modern agriculture, as we know it, cannot survive without the tractor and its varied implements.

1. Modern Agriculture vs. Natural Agriculture

The current model for agriculture started out with the best of intentions: Produce more food for a growing population while shifting the work force to more valuable sectors like industry, manufacturing and high-tech jobs. Attempts were made to help the developing nations tool up to produce more food with less effort.

However, things aren't improving. Throughout the world food production is becoming less and less reliable, more fragile, and increasingly toxic. Agriculture has been used to mortgage our future. With the modern banking system's need for expansion, small farms have gone through waves of mergers and acquisitions only Wall Street would understand. Developing countries have sold their birthright to high-tech, high-debt, mono-crop systems that have a built in expiration date. The chemical industry has ridden piggyback on the beast and taken its profits, but the farmlands are spent.

Natural Farming is the most economical way to solve this impending global food problem. We are approaching a two-fold global crisis in food production, as both the quantity and quality is declining. There is an economically viable way to make crop fertilizers and livestock feed from waste products that are currently being lost to the environment.

The pollution from pesticides and herbicides contained in produce is well documented. As different feed-born pathogens devastate livestock in developed countries, people are growing concerned about the industrial processes that are causing this problem. It is now also a problem in developing countries. The growing dilemma is affecting human health as witnessed in the rise of "diseases of the rich."

As people in outlying communities become accustomed to the modern food packaging and distribution system, they are suffering from all the ailments of their richer city dwelling counterparts. From diabetes to gout to cancers, rural folk who used to grow 90% of their food supply now specialize in only 1 or 2 commodities and buy their daily food stocks from the stores. This is increasing their health risk, as they gobble down large quantities of refined processed white sugar and fiberless white flour as well as high fat, high salt canned goods or completely processed meals.

Most countries are now *fast food nations,* as they adapt their local palates to nutritionally poor franchise foods. Franchisers economize on ingredients with even less nutritional value than equivalent foods in the developed countries they are copying. In addition, deteriorating health reflects exactly what the new diet is worth. Children rarely experience wholesome foods. They dunk their donuts and dip their chips in ignorance as they feast on a bold new diet for a new age.

Starting out small in the green house prepares the plant for bigger things later.

Natural Farming considers the biological aspects as an equal in importance to the natural chemical processes of food production.

Reusing plastic cups from the fast food industry in the nursery is a form of recycling.

The current paradigm is man centered. The modern theory of agriculture claims that plants are nothing more than chemical assemblies of basic inert ingredients. They expound that we can isolate the chemicals and sell them to the farmer, and then they can feed the plant directly. The petroleum industry has done quite well with this approach, making food growers ever dependent on the large manufacturers of fertilizer inputs. This added cost has taken away the autonomy of the small hold farmer and forced many into endless debt cycles. These schemes cause farmers to increase land area and production so they can justify the mechanization and high cost of inputs. *Farmers* who sit in board meetings and make decisions based on profitability studies or return on investment analysis run the largest farms in Europe and North America. Food quality and nutrition takes a back seat to satisfying investors and shareholders.

Through this man centered paradigm we have been trained to see the chemical side of growing food with almost total neglect of the biological side. We feed the plant directly with chemicals. The problems of nutrient run off, nutrient loss through volatilization and the destruction of beneficial microorganisms, insects, birds and reptiles have been largely ignored. The biological processes in the soil and plant are rarely taken into consideration in this prevailing system. Farmers are trained to add more chemicals when plants are struggling to survive. This is a post symptomatic approach to disease and pest management that makes farmers more dependent on their suppliers.

It is my opinion that this model has failed on a global level. The developing countries on this planet can't afford to bring to market the food they need. Something is terribly wrong. Here in the Philippines, the small hold farmer can no longer afford the hybrid rice seed, urea, complete fertilizer, triple phosphate, and fungicide and still cover his labor. By the time he harvests, he has no profit and little food surplus to live on. He needs a real job just to cover his full time hobby growing rice!

The Philippines is host to I.R.R.I., the International Rice Research Institute, and yet is importing rice from Vietnam. It has an annual short fall because of poorer yields in existing regions. This is also due to lower net production because fewer new farmers replace the farmers who give up on rice growing.

The answer is not in modifying genetics. Playing with the created order of things is not wise. Let's face it; modern theory has led us into this mess. It has failed for the last fifty years; how can we expect good results now? We keep experimenting on consumers only to find out the problems in subsequent years, long after things can be reversed. The foundation is wrong. The assumptions are flawed.

It's time to get back to the fundamentals of agriculture, sustainable agriculture. Natural farming involves efforts to simulate the natural environment to stabilize our food production. The key is to build on sound, scientific principles that will increase fertility in the soil. This will bring about healthy plants, insect resistant plants that will produce high quality food while feeding the worker, family, community and world. We do that by simulating a climax vegetative state which we can grow food, like the forest. However, we don't destroy the rain forest; we study it. The forest is an incredible University for learning from, not experimenting with. We experiment on our soil and with our plants.

Recycled soda cups make for good potting cups. Technically, we are recycling by re-using discarded waste from the fast food industry. We always reduce, recycle, reuse or refuse to buy it in the first place.

At Aloha House we are using many different solutions to address some of the problems we are all facing as populations grow. We can't reverse the destruction that is outside our influence, but we can have an effect on our immediate area of influence. We are able to make a difference if we have good information, a reasoned approach and a foundation to build upon.

We need to build on a sure foundation, not on shifting sand. Farmers read a little and hear a lot. We get into trouble when we don't do our homework. We can't farm by rumor. We need to get a hold of the information behind all the data that is flowing from the journals, media and Internet. We have a large volume of scientific data available, but most farmers don't know how to use it. To quote Mr. Hoffman: *"we are data rich but information poor"*. It's time to assess the state of modern agriculture and see what the options are from a fresh perspective.

We have many nutritious plants that we grow for forage crops and compost as well as human consumption. Livestock convert our surplus production and crop wastes into high profit meat products that are without toxins or chemical residue.

There can be billions of microorganisms in a handful of soil.

2. The Soil Is the Foundation

In our seminars we teach the fundamentals of Sustainable Agriculture. Some call it Organic Farming, some Nature Farming, others Natural Farming. There are subtleties that can make them a little different, but the commitment is to safe, quality food production without chemical inputs. If we feed the soil organic matter, then the microbes will feed the plant. Pest and disease management can be obtained naturally. Building up the soil and managing the organic matter as it is converted into humus is an age-old method.

Humus is the rich, sticky, yet crumbly substance found in healthy soil that is the world's greatest resource. It has to be properly managed, preserved and can be increased through microbial activity that converts organic matter from roots, compost, manure or crop residue mulched on the surface or plowed under as a green fertilizer.

Did you know rain forests never get "sick"? That's right. They have reached a climax vegetative state that keeps them stable permanently. If you don't kill all the grazers, prairies can function indefinitely also. That's why indigenous North Americans used natural grass fires to keep the land productive. A localized forest fire can create better forest as it burns off undergrowth and releases certain nutrients locked up in the cellulose. Even humus and peat can burn if one is not careful.

Of course when systems are altered unnaturally, things go bad rather quickly. As soon as we disturb the soil, clear trees or concentrate livestock, we have special management challenges. Natural farming is a bit of an oxymoron because tilling soil by the hectare isn't natural. Once you plow or rearrange the soil, it is unnatural, but we can copy the systems that help our plants grow. We can simulate the forest floor effect by using the ten fundamentals discussed later in this book.

Practices such as minimal tillage and inoculating with beneficial microorganisms quickly build up effective soil systems that have the structure, nutrients and microbial balance to produce food for generations to come. By adding organic matter in the soil and on the surface, the soil is fed. Actually, it is the microbes in the soil that consume the sugars, nitrogen, complex carbohydrates, fats, and all the other goodies that accumulate in topsoil. They excrete amino acids, root dividing hormones, anti-oxidants etc. This in turn is made bio-available to the roots in the rhizosphere (root zone) down in the soil. That's why we say; "feed the soil, don't feed the plant."

Biologically, soil is a complex food web that creates stability when properly fed and nurtured.

Dr. Elaine Ingram, who is the founder of Soil Food Web Inc., http://www.soilfoodweb.com, is a leading proponent of bacterial and fungal balance through proper composting, inoculation, testing and regular monitoring. She teaches her farmer-clients to supplement their organic practices by using high quality composts, fed with molasses, fish emulsions, and trace elements while being aerated. Called ACT, aerated compost teas populate to high numbers while crowding out pathogens. The finished tea is sprayed throughout the farm or garden. She emphasizes high fungal counts for perennial plants, orchards and trees, while higher bacteria counts can be obtained from specialized compost teas for vegetables and annuals. They even test and review compost, soil, and tea as well as tea brewers.

Ancient inoculation systems have been very useful for small-scale applications. Both Korean and Japanese farmers have been gathering soil from the forest floor and mixing it with rice bran. They utilize a process of fermentation for favorable composting and propagation of large numbers and varieties of microorganisms. This is anaerobic composting without disease build up or foul odors.

They place the mixed soil and bran into clay jars for up to one month, and then use it in their farm system. They also make garlic and ginger extracts for insect control. Often referred to as KIMCHI farming, this method has proven the powerful effect microbes can have on a simulated natural environment. Their techniques have been utilized for their foliar sprays more than soil management. They have a soil treatment with rice bran and microbes, but for unknown reasons, it is not being promoted at this time.

The Korean method still thrives to this day. We have used the complete system with success and continue to integrate components of this ancient technology in our cropping and livestock operation.

The Japanese word for fermented plant matter is BOKASHI. We have adapted a formula for use in the Philippines utilizing industrial wastes such as coconut (copra) meal, rice bran, charcoal and manures. The formula is highly adaptable and will be discussed at length later in this book.

Korean Natural Farming – We started our microbial program by multiplying beneficial microbes through anaerobic fermentation in clay jars.

Professor Teruo Higa, at the University of Ryukyus, Okinawa, Japan, has studied and isolated the naturally occurring beneficials for large-scale utilization. His method is to group different families of microbes together to form a cohesive unit, a symbiotic consortium of compatible microbes that keep out disease and efficiently convert waste into wonderful organic amendments, feed stock, and fertilizers. This is one way we build up our soil for the long run.

He has proposed a soil classification based not on structure, but on microbial health. The soil is classified according to the types of microorganisms present, including beneficial microorganisms. The most productive of the 4 classes: a soil that is not just disease suppressing, but zymogenic, able to influence plants so that they grow into disease resistant champions. He focuses on the oxidative and fermentative by-products the microbial colony produces.

Higa has packaged the technology and priced it according to the economy of each nation it is produced in. There are over 50 countries that sell Dr. Higa's Effective Microorganisms (EM1) through the Effective Microorganisms Research Organization (EMRO). They all contain hundreds of different beneficial species, with 3 main families of microorganisms. They are all naturally occurring and not modified at the genetic level (Non-GMO). In the US they are OMRI approved as organic inputs. Completely safe, these little workers are like soil livestock. They are not chemicals, but a living consortium of microbes that convert waste into plant food, root dividing hormones, amino acids, etc. EM1 also works as a probiotic in livestock.

Dr. Higa found the phototrophs indispensable to the technology. These photosynthetic microbes synthesize sunlight when applied to leaves, thus enhancing the UV utilization. They convert the sun energy into plant food that will be taken in through the leaves pours (stomata). The microbes produce foliar feed, but they are not fertilizer. Most batches contain Rhodopsudomonas sp., Rotobactors, and like species of Purple Non Sulfur Bacteria (PNSB), because of their adaptability in different environments.

They can actually work without UV in an oxygen free vessel or buried in soil or compost. Anaerobically, these adaptable little agents use heat energy instead of sunlight to convert organic matter into fertilizer or higher quality feed. They must be present in sufficient quantities. Molds, Actinomycetes, and fungi are found in a typical mix of EM1. They are important because they convert cellulose into outstanding soil components like humus, humic acids, mycelium, etc. That means the finished product is *high-quality-crumbly-rich-friable-compost*. Lactic acid bacteria make lactic acid. These surgeons of the microbial world biologically exclude pathogens by out eating the competition. You don't need to kill off the bad guys, just starve them out by radically outnumbering them with the beneficials. They all work together to stabilize the soil and produce great food while minimizing disease. They are part of an overall program that is helping tropical farmers succeed with lower risk. They help build up the soil if properly inoculated. Let's see how we do it here at Aloha House.

The Backpack Sprayer is standardized in Asia. It holds 4 gallons or 15 liters and is easy to repair. We can always find replacement parts. It can be refilled efficiently and is economical; one man can cover up to 2 hectares using this clever invention.

3. Co-infect: The Art of Inoculation

There are billions of microbes in a handful of soil. 90% of these microbes are neutral; they don't affect the soil toward disease or health when left on their own. However, according to Dr. Higa, in abused or diseased-chemical based soils, 5 to 10% of the overall colony is pathogenic made up of disease causing organisms. They steer the neutral microbes and create low productivity. Some soils are so bad that less than 1% of the organisms are beneficial.

The dominant pathogens lead the neutrals into rot, decay and disease with great inefficiency. All we have to do to turn the tables is out number the bad guys with the good guys. Beneficial and effective microorganisms will take over the helm and direct the neutrals into a balanced productive state. We don't need to disinfect, rather we co-infect. Overwhelm the bad guys through foliar sprays, soil drenches and compost treatments. In livestock housing we spray the bedding, cement and walls. The EM will work to biologically exclude the pathogens as well as minimize methane gasses and ammonia.

Think of biological exclusion as a litter of hungry puppy dogs. Let's say the mother has a shortage of teats and two pups can't feed properly. The little guys will not be killed by some battle of the best. Rather, the smaller will be excluded by the bigger; the better feeders that have the ability to compete for the food source will prosper. If the bigger pups get all the milk, the others will be held to a nominal role in the pack and may even die from lack of nutrients.

It's the same in the soil. The beneficials don't have to do battle; rather they out eat and out compete against the pathogens, because of their design. This is the synergistic value of microbial stability. There is constant antagonism to the pathogens by way of food monopolization. That means balance is achieved with the natural order coming into equilibrium.

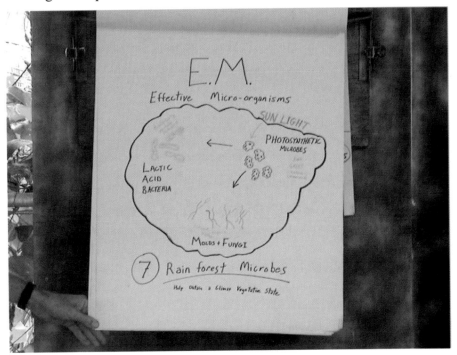

The EM consortium prevents disease and also builds up natural immune systems in the host plant as they co-prosper symbiotically. We don't need to disinfect; we co-infect.

We call this co-infecting, outnumbering the bad guys with the good guys. The neutrals follow the lead of the dominant controlling system. You should not disinfect. This will kill the beneficials, the neutral majority and the pathogens all at once. It's the destructive ones that always return first. Just outnumber the pathogens with beneficial microbes.

It's like politics. We have all observed that choosing good leaders allows the citizens to prosper. Corrupt governments always lead the people into graft and corruption. Honesty seems to be the first casualty in survival. Politicians are less than 5% of the populace (hopefully), yet they can guide the masses, an entire nation, to success or failure in one administration. It will take much more effort to turn it back around. Microbial management is the same; today's management practices affect future crops. If we outnumber the bad with the good we will eventually succeed. If we *radically* outnumber the bad with the good we will succeed more quickly.

The Three Way Model of Microbial Management chart below shows you how valuable it is to inoculate in the beginning of your project. Use beneficial microorganisms in your natural system at the start, or to help in converting from chemical use. It only has limited effects on systems where fungicides and pesticides have been sprayed, because chemicals disinfect the entire area of application.

Table 1 – Three Way Model of Microbial Management

The Three Way Model Of Microbial Management		
Inoculation without Natural Inputs	Traditional Organic Method	Sustainable Inoculation Method
NO RETURN on investment	SLOW RETURN on investment	FASTER RETURN on investment
If you use microbes on depleted soil, with low organic matter, and no natural inputs, then the microbes have nothing to transform and success is not obtained.	Traditional organic farming adds organic matter to the soil, but it can take 4-5 years for the microbes to show up and make the soil profitable.	Inoculate from the beginning with a wide variety of symbiotic microbes. They work as a team; success can be seen in the first year, without major lose of productivity.

EM contains some of the following organisms; photosynthetic bacteria, lactic acid bacteria, yeasts, Actinomycetes and fermenting fungi. In EM literature, the key idea is that the microbes form a consortium, a group that works as a team. They all work better with each other rather than alone. The photosynthetic bacteria are also known as phototrophs, Rhodopsudomonas sp., Rotobactor, PNSBs (Purple Non Sulfur Bacteria) and seem to guide the hundreds of other microbes in a beneficially productive state. There are now many manufacturers of EM like inoculants. Some of the best available have the proper balance of LAS, phototrophs, molds and fungi for the region they are prepared in. Most of these cultures are already available through commercial suppliers to the food industry, brewers and scientific community.

Co-infect in the nursery and green house to keep plants strong and healthy. We add high anti-oxidant ingredients like ginger, garlic, chili and neem for natural insect management.

Effective Microorganisms consist of a wide variety of beneficial organisms. The white molds are a sign of healthy processes in the soil or compost.

They crowd out pathogens and minimize odors and disease. The pioneer and discoverer of EM is a professor in Japan, Dr. Higa. According to EM materials:

Photosynthetic bacteria support the activities of other microorganisms. The photosynthetic bacteria also utilize substances produced by other microorganisms. This phenomenon is termed "coexistence and co-prosperity".

When Effective Microorganisms increase as a community in soils, populations of native effective microorganisms are also enhanced. Thus, the micro flora becomes rich and microbial ecosystems in the soil become well balanced. Specific microorganisms, harmful ones, do not increase. Thus, soil borne diseases are suppressed.

Plant roots secrete substances such as carbohydrates, amino and organic acids, and active enzymes. Effective microorganisms use these secretions for growth. During this process, they also secrete and provide amino and nucleic acids, a variety of vitamins and hormones to plants.

Furthermore, in such soils, effective microorganisms in the root zone co-exist (symbiosis) with plants, feeding each other. Plants grow exceptionally well in soils that are dominated by effective microorganisms.

The favorite specie seems to be the Rhodopseudomonas sp., and various Rhodobactor species. These microbes convert, or synthesize, sunlight when applied to plant leaves.

Through its leaves, the plant utilizes the waste from the microbes. They are not a fertilizer, but they make fertilizer. When buried in soil and composts they retrieve their energy from heat instead of sunlight. The Creator made some highly adaptable switch-hitters; they are key players in fermentative systems. However, they need organic matter to do their job.

Organic matter is previously living components from the natural world. This includes leaves and roots, bark and hulls, grass and straw. Manures, bones, seashells and rock powders can also be included. Chemicals such as Malathion and urea do not qualify.

The reason we had success in our system early on was due to adding as much organic matter as economically possible in the beginning, while inoculating with the beneficial microbes. Truckloads of manure were composted with seaweed or rice mill waste. We sprayed them, poured them, mixed them and fed them to the soil, to the compost, to the leaves, and to the bark. Now our compost needs are being met by farm-generated fertility. In addition, we spray less often than at the beginning.

Fungi and mushrooms are helpful in the soil.

After you have been spraying with beneficial microorganisms for a few months and quit using chemicals, you will start to see mushrooms. Don't be alarmed! This is a sign of a healthy ecology and they are good for the soil. The mushroom is the fruiting body from miles of mycelium crawling through your layers of organic matter and topsoil.

Fungi help break down courser material and make it available to bacteria. Fungi break down the high carbon content components like wood fiber and bark while enriching the soil for perennials and trees. Bacteria create a favorable habitat for annuals such as vegetables. The entire food web is multiple cycles of dismantling and building food for your plants.

Horticulturist Simon Gill joins us at Aloha House in some of the advanced trainings, showing students how to succeed in growing the appropriate varieties for their climate and soil conditions.

I have cataloged the ten most effective means of adding and managing this organic matter into the soil. This organic matter is the feedstock for your microbes. Consider the microbial colonies in your soil as miniature livestock; living in the earth and grazing on your organic matter. Your microbial composition needs to have diversity to process the organic matter you keep layering up with each fundamental. They need to be in balance so they can work hard to bring you good food. I now call these main principles the Ten Fundamentals of Sustainable Agriculture. There are many variations but the principles are timeless. We will look at these basic ideas in the coming chapters, but first, let's prepare our microbes.

El Nido Foundation attends our weekly seminar on Sustainable Agriculture. We have a nominal materials fee for the course. This weeds out the idle and curious and motivates students to practice what they learn.

At Aloha House's advanced training- Students are always seeking more practical knowledge. The lecture phase is supplemented with video course work, a flip chart presentation and hands on application. We finish with a working tour of our organic farm. Our internship program is gaining interest also.

4. Hands On- EM Extended

I t's time for some hands on farming. This step makes inoculation affordable to the masses. We will grow some microbes. We call this EM Extended. We will make a concoction that used to take me 27 man-hours to make and weeks to watch and monitor while propagating. I had to grow each organism individually. It was labor intensive, as well as expensive. Let me explain.

The Korean Natural Farming (KNF) System is a highly effective inoculation method. We learned to gather and propagate our own microbes. We successfully applied these principles to our crops at Aloha House and saw good results. This is part of a bigger movement called I.M., which stands for Indigenous Microorganisms. It has an influence in organics; however, the extreme form of this movement is to culture only the microbes from your own farm, without bringing in any of the *evil* foreign microbes from non-indigenous regions. I find this an unbalanced approach.

The problem with the above theory is two fold. First, microbes are not indigenous, not in the same sense that we would apply the word to plants and wildlife. The spores and colonies of most varieties of microbes will inhabit any area that favors their growth. They are very difficult to contain. The beneficial ones don't need to be contained. They will only improve your soil and co-exist with the other beneficials and guide the neutrals to better use.

We are learning the hard way that eradicated diseases like small pox or polio are coming back. Most microbes are universal, often found in the smallest amounts throughout the world. Even on the surface of your skin can be found e-coli, hepatitis and typhoid at parts per billion. Nature brings balance and will control by keeping the unproductive species minimized, not eradicated. Even undesirable organisms produce beneficial aspects to a system at optimized minimal levels. Everything in creation has an optimum level. So beneficial microbes may prosper better in some climates and microclimates, but we don't need to fear which ones are indigenous. What we want are the ones that will build up the soil and protect our plants.

The second concern with the IM movement extremes is that you don't have large quantities of all the beneficials that you need to succeed economically in your system. They just are not there. That's why we are inoculating, to bring in all the species we need, not just exploit some that we can find on our project.

So that being said, let's just open up a bottle of dormant EM type microbial concoction and propagate them one (1) generation. We can't keep repeating this procedure because we will loose the balance in the population and we will not benefit from our efforts. You will need to buy one bottle of EM1 (you will use 45 ml.), 45 ml. molasses, 1 liter of non-chlorinated water and an empty 1 liter plastic bottle (P.E.T. bottles work well).

E.M.E. MATERIALS / INGREDIENTS LIST

- 45 ml. EM1, 45 ml. molasses
- 1 liter of non-chlorinated water
- 1 liter empty plastic bottle (P.E.T. bottles work good)
- Permanent marker
- 1 Tablespoon- 1T (15 ml.)

Buy your TABLE SPOON (T) from the kitchen store. It can't be the ordinary dining spoon from your dinner table. This is not accurate, nor is it standardized. Women who cook know this, but you guys need to get the right stuff, OK? We always teach our students to calibrate a 1-liter bottle; you can do it with 45ml. (3T=45 ml.) of water and mark the level. Then we pour out the water and add molasses directly into the bottle. Don't measure the molasses into spoons or pour through a funnel, as it is very sticky and will make a mess of things. Always use molasses because it has the best nutrients for your microbes.

We trained 50 students from Western Palawan University, in Aborlan, to make their own EM culture.

Then dilute the molasses by adding about half the water and gently shaking. Take care not to aggravate the solution; avoid creating foam.

Next add 45 ml. EM1 and the rest of the water. Fill to the shoulder of the bottle, allow some head space for fermentation to take place. Then label the cap with a permanent marker. Write EME and include the day and month. Let the gas out every morning and in one week you have a huge quantity of EM for the price of 45 ml. Remember: don't extend the EME, it will not remain true to the mother culture.

If you end up having older EME on hand, that's O.K.; don't throw it out! The anti-oxidant value increases over time and helps in odor control. You can use older batches for minimizing foul smells from waste problems. It is excellent in shredded materials; feed it to the compost. The flexibility of the system prevents you from ever making a mistake that cannot be remediated through a natural process.

Shredders increase the surface area of organic matter and allow microorganisms to feed efficiently. Microbes need food, moisture and air for aerobic composting. A shredder will accelerate the aerobic composting process.

That's one of the comforting aspects of EM technology; a solution in one area often leads to solutions in other areas. You don't have to worry about creating some kind of Frankenstein; the risk is virtually zero on health and environment. It is even approved by O.M.R.I., the Organic Materials Review Institute. They provide certifiers, growers, manufacturers and suppliers an independent review of products intended for use in certified organic production, handling, and processing.

Molasses is food for the EM family. The lactic acid bacteria, such as Lactobacillus, consumes the sugars and causes the EM to go dormant, granting a stable shelf life.

Be sure to make what you need in advance, but don't over stock. For maximum microbial activity you should use it up in the coming months. The shelf life is variable with the extension time depending on ingredient quality, water source, ambient temperature and elevation. In the tropics the whole process is easy to oversee. Over all, it's a low maintenance operation. We just keep a stock ready, on hand for use. Our pattern of use is very predictable now.

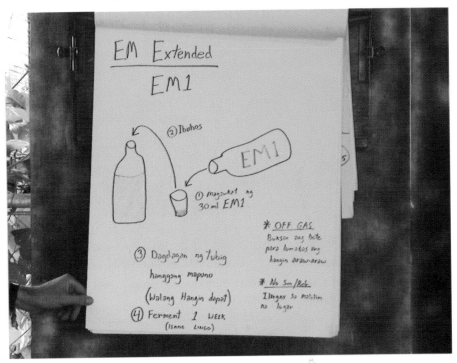

Our training is hands on, including a mixing session where you learn to extend the EM1 one generation, lowering the cost of inoculation for the small farmer.

It is worth noting, however, that without a properly organized approach, you can waste a lot of time. You need to be disciplined when implementing these principles. My goal is that by the end of this book, you will have some useful information and motivation to go about successfully transforming your agricultural endeavors, or at least, assimilating a few of the principles and technologies as presented here in this volume.

Microbial applications are safe for humans to make. Pets, livestock or aquariums will benefit from the effects of EM.

Science is fun - These students are enjoying the EM experience. Measuring your own water, molasses and EM-1 for mixing, blending and fermenting brings down your costs. It's an inexpensive solution for your farm or livestock unit.

Students get to examine bokashi as an alternative fertilizer.

My son Archie joins a student and me in a foray of mad science. Mixing
EM1 is safe for children as well as for older farmers.

Spraying with a mixture of beneficial microorganisms is effective if it is a rich culture of different symbiotic species.

5. Basic Inoculation

EM Extended is now ready to use as a diluted solution. It's part of the Big Solution. If you feed the soil and manage it according to the 10 Fundamentals you will see tangible results. We will discuss these fundamentals in the following chapters. Let's go over the basic application procedure for EM Extended first. Then I will tell you how we do it at Aloha House. Once you have the hang of it, there are more advanced applications.

We started by spraying every week. For livestock, spraying the yard daily may be necessary to control odors in the beginning. There is more concentrated waste. Spraying daily will help out the first week.

You will catch up on the backlog of problems from previous management. We had a backpack sprayer which was very easy to use and replacement parts were easy to come by. We used it so often that we wore out our sprayer handle. Larger operation may spray monthly and still see good results.

The power sprayer makes a fine mist to distribute your microbes. Be sure to keep the setting around 10 bars or you will damage the microbes and limit the effectiveness.

Then we graduated to an electric pressure sprayer with a 100-meter hose that winds up onto a reel. It's a very handy accoutrement. It makes it a lot easier to spray our 8,000 sq. m (2-acre) growing and grazing areas. We have the garden house and nursery centrally located. In it we have a 200 L (50 Gal.) drum for mixing our various concoctions, so we can reach the entire spread with our sprayer. During rainy weeks we spray every Monday and Friday.

The sprayer also comes in a gasoline or diesel version so that you can mount it on a tractor or utility vehicle for mobile spraying. We use 1 drum for very 1 hectare (2.5 acres), so a large system would need to carry the liquid too. Foliar application is 200 to 500 parts water to 1 part EME. For soil treatment you can increase the concentration to 100 parts water to 1 part EME. That would allow you to cover more area with less fluid sloshing around and less refills as well. We don't spray more than 200:1 on plants, as it is possible to burn them due to the acid level of the EM. Once it grows in the environment it actually works as a buffer through organic matter, but in it's dormant state the pH is 3.5.

Table 2- EM Diluted, or EMA, or AEM

Use	Size	EME	Molasses	Water
Plants 1:1:500	16 Liter Backpack Sprayer	30 ml	30 ml	15 Liters
Plants 1:1:500	50 gallon (200 Liter) Drum	400 ml	400 ml	199 Liters
Livestock 1:100	15 Liter Backpack Sprayer	150 ml	NONE	15 Liters
Livestock 1:100	50 gallon (200 Liter) Drum	2 Liters	NONE	198 Liters

Follow the recommended concentrations to start with. Livestock concentrations can be higher than for agriculture use. We use molasses for agriculture. In some regions they call it E.M.A.S. (EM Activated Solution). Others call it AEM, Activated EM. Basically, we're giving the microbes additional nutrients when we send them off to work. We premix the AEM 2-12 hours ahead of use, usually overnight. In the USA they call EME by the confusing term EMAS. They are cautious to call it EM *EXTENDED* because it will not propagate a second time. It will be inferior to the original EM1 and you would be wasting your efforts.

So basic inoculation is pretty simple, the more often you spray, up to a point, the sooner you succeed. Some large systems spray only once per month or less, it depends on the crop and management system you have as well as soil conditions, season and climate. Just take good notes and keep a keen eye on what you are doing. Later we will discuss how to enhance your EME to increase its effectiveness. First, we have to feed the soil. So let's start with the Ten Fundamentals!

We inoculate the pig house using a backpack sprayer. Spray weekly for small-scale livestock to minimize odors and diseases.

Table 3- EM Economics

Conventional backpack sprayer- 4 gallons or 15 liters

EM 1	EM E	Back Pack Sprayer	Ml/sq. M	Area Covered
	30 ml.	1	100	150 m^2
30 ml.	1 L.	33	100	4,950 m^2
1 L.	30 L.	1,000	100	15 Hectares

The economy of EM speaks for itself. One bottle covers a lot of area. Just 30 ml. of EM1 makes 1 liter of EM Extended which makes 33 backpack sprayers, which covers ½ hectare or 1.25 Acres. A bottle of EM1, extended and diluted, will cover 15 hectares or 37 acres.

EM 1	EM E	200 L Drum	ml/m^2	Area Covered
	400 ml.	1	100	2000 m^2
1 L.	30 L.	75	100	15 Hectares

We fill a 200-liter drum and use a power sprayer to cover our farm.

Seedlings respond well to compost teas and EM sprays. We cover them every week with millions of beneficial species. We also make our own fruit flytraps for the nursery. Microbial sprays are only part of an overall solution.

Bringing fresh, tasty, high quality food to the market is very rewarding to the grower. When you practice the fundamentals, a profitable venture is assured.

6. The Ten Fundamentals

We gardeners, farmers and food growers are always looking for new technology, but a large body of information is already available to us. When I scan resources from A to Z, I find many interesting titles that are widely published and now available from Amazon books, Acres USA, ATTRA and various world wide web internet sites. I see a consensus forming. The material promotes certain ideas and concepts.

There appeared to be 8-12 main themes on soil management, natural fertility, cropping systems, etc. We adapted much of what we read in principle, adjusting for our particular tropical climate and clay soil structure. We quickly learned which local substitutions were appropriate.

In order to present these topics to our growing number of students interested in natural farming and EM technology, we put it all together in a course we now call "Introduction to Sustainable Agriculture, Natural Farming in Palawan." The core of the course is now available in DVD format and can be ordered from our resources in the back of this book. In our seminars we teach the 10 Fundamentals of Sustainable Agriculture. The following chapters summarize what individual books can better cover. Crop rotation, legume usage, companion planting and composting are a few of them.

The main *principle* is to feed the soil. Inoculation is the *means* of quickly stabilizing your system. Through microbial action the plants will have all they need. The 10 Fundamentals tell you *how* to feed and

manage the soil. These 10 building blocks will create a storehouse of organic matter that will become humus and give you better soil, hence better yields.

Take note how each fundamental has variations, with certain schools of thought specializing in 2 or 3 fundamentals. For certain crop or livestock systems, we can

Active experimentation and a keen eye for details help the organic grower identify the best formulas and practices for his project.

economize our efforts. For long-range sustainability, we need to practice these concepts till they become second nature. Integrate these schemes so that you know them by intimate practice, not just theory.

There is some overlap in my 10 fundamentals. In addition, I'm quite good at forcing other agricultural practices into one of them. However, I'm always learning new techniques and enjoy classifying them. For example, a legume in rotation with corn can be plowed under. You are actually double dipping. You are gaining fertility twice as fast. You see, the legume is fundamental #2, legume usage. Corn follows it, and crop rotation is fundamental #1.

Plowed under, it becomes a green fertilizer, #5, which is actually a form of composting, #4, done out in the field instead of in a pile. In addition, if your legume was clover or alfalfa, it qualifies as a cover crop, #7! See the incredible storehouse of fertility released when we learn to use these 10 basic strategies to our advantage?

If I were to arrange these farm practices in order of effort expended or energy spent, from low sweat to high sweat, this is how I would do it:

Subjective Ordering of the Fundamentals
(From least labor to most labor)

1. Proper crop rotation to beat the disease and pest cycle-

This one is a no brainer. Just plant different families of crops and you will eliminate many problems. God made us smarter than the insects for a reason.

2. Legume usage for nitrogen fixation-

Think free fertilizer! Select the proper species and you won't need chemical fertilizers. Let the nitrogen appear out-of-thin-air!

5. Companion planting (inter cropping) for insect control, etc.-

Low energy planning is all it takes. Then you won't need pesticides. Deciding which crops should neighbor each other is called companion planting. Planning which plants should follow each other is called crop rotation.

9. Insect Habitat for beneficial species; bait crops for the bad guys- This requires more planning for planting, but low energy to maintain because they are perennials.

Microbial Management with foliar spray and soil treatment etc.- Takes a little more effort and requires more management.

7. Cover cropping to conserve topsoil and moisture [living mulch-

More effort planting, but it won't kill you.

3. Green fertilizers to feed the next crop efficiently- Properly plowing a crop under takes considerable effort, but it's worth it!

8. Minimal Tillage- Preserve soil life and structure, save labor-

Deep digging or raising your vegetable beds takes some work on your part, but once the beds are established, you're mainly top dressing your compost and drilling your seed directly or transplanting. No more plowing!

6. Mulching to conserve topsoil and moisture-

This takes some work, gathering and spreading your cover over the exposed soil, but it saves you from weeding and watering.

The herb crew comes down the mountain with some Chinese parsley, Indian coriander and garlic chives.

10. Animal Integration -fertilizer source as well as food production-

Livestock takes some getting used to if you don't know a buck from a stud, but they are well worth the time and energy expended.

4. Composting to build up Humus [aerobic, anaerobic, vermicast]-

Compost is King. This is where the work will kill you, if you don't do it properly. Once you learn my methods, you will have more time to oversee the rest of your project!

You could also order these 10 fundamentals according to the economic value that you receive per man-hour of labor. For us it would be ordered from most valuable to least: 4-10-2-8-3-7-6-1-9-5. Think them though after you read the book. What other ways would you prioritize them? You could rate them according to nitrogen value, potassium, or other nutrients generated.

Let's examine each fundamental according to the order I teach them to everyday farmers. This order makes it easiest for me to convey these concepts. I build on each principle, one at a time. Then, once we grasp them, we can shuffle them around all we want. We will examine crop rotation first, because all the old farmers remember using this technique. It was popular at one time, but with mechanized mono

cropping, it is less common. In the next chapter, you will see why this fundamental is important.

Lettuce greens and red radishes are rotated with 40 other vegetables, herbs and fruits to keep the production stable and the quality high. We use different radishes for salads and kimchi.

When you change the planting order and diversify, you are enhancing the natural resistance of your crops.

7. Crop Rotation

P roper crop rotation is *Fundamental #1*. It will beat the disease and pest cycle while promoting nutrient cycling. This is a forgotten age-old method to assure the health of future crops. It is of the utmost importance to minimize nutrient loss for long-range success.

When the same plant is continually grown in the same place, then the same nutrients are required. This will exhaust certain nutrients, depending on the crop. When different crops are grown in rotation, the nutrients, such as trace elements, will not be as quickly depleted. Deep-rooted plants will bring up more elements from deeper layers of sub-soil. When used as green fertilizer or compost they will return trace minerals and nutrients to the topsoil for future plantings of shallower feeders.

Even a grass pasture will improve when it is in rotation with a legume like alfalfa, mungo beans, perennial peanuts or clover.

The old farmers remember this. During our training seminars the lolas and kuyas (older guys) admit that in Mindanao or Luzon their father used to grow peanuts or beans when they were between rice crops. It's common knowledge for most farmers, but they don't understand the full benefits of the concept and are no longer told to practice this principle. When people understand *why*, they are more likely to implement the method and realize the benefit from the effects of this fundamental.

Crop rotation also breaks the disease cycle when a different crop is planted. Many diseases are not able to find a new host plant when the rotation utilizes a different family each time. Do not follow rice with corn, as both are in the grass family and can have some of the same disease problems.

We interrupt destructive insect cycles with crop rotation too. For example, up in the rainforest, the shifting cultivators will use a cleared area for only 2 years. The first planting of maize is spectacular, so they plant it again. As they deplete the nutrients they get lower yields. They also develop a large number of pests. The first crop will not have any stem borer damage. These pests will lay eggs that feed on the next batch of maize. By the third or fourth continual cropping, they have a plague of biblical proportions. When a different crop is planted each rotation, then the insect pests are not able to find a new host plant in that area. They may hatch in great numbers, but they don't survive in significant populations on the journey to the next host.

We just have to be smarter than insects. Change their diet and they starve to death or die off in the process of relocating. In natural farming, we don't have to battle fiercely and kill off the undesirables directly; we exclude them biologically by changing their habitat or feedstock. It was our all-knowing Creator who made us smart, but greedy techniques are ruining us. In our efforts to produce more for less, we are growing dependent on chemicals that reduce the overall quality of our produce and pollute our bodies at the same time. The insects keep coming back. They build immunities to the palliatives we use. Rotation works best with a different family each time. Do not follow tomatoes with potatoes, as both are in the same family and have many of the same pest problems. Below is a list of some of the families we are seeing in the farms around us.

Our vegetative strips have a wide variety of crops in rotation to prevent the build up of both pests and diseases.

Cauliflower is a real challenge to grow in the tropics, but with specialized netting and shading, it does surprisingly well.

FAMILIES of COMMON CROPS for ROTATION

Grass family (Gramineae):

Rice (palay), corn, sugar cane, oats, wheat, and other cereal crops.

Cabbage family (Cruciferae):

Bok choy, pechay and other Asian greens, broccoli, Brussels sprouts, cabbage, cauliflower, collard, kale, kohlrabi, mustard, radish, turnip.

Legume family (Leguminosae):

All beans, pulses and peas (sitaw, mung bean), peanuts, cover crops such as kudzo, perennial peanut (mani-mani), alfalfa, clovers, and vetch. Perennials Legume Shrubs - rensonii, flemingia.

Trees- Kakawati (Madre de cacao), Ipil-Ipil, fire tree.

Allium family (Alliaceae):
Garlic, leeks, onion, shallots

Daisy family (Compositae):
Chamomile, chicory, dandelion, endive, globe artichoke, Jerusalem artichoke, lettuce, salsify, sunflowers

Carrot or Parsley family (Umbelliferae):
Carrots, celery, celeriac, coriander, caraway, dill, fennel, parsley, parsnips

Beet family (Chenopodiaceae):
Beet, spinach, Swiss chard, lamb's quarters

Gourd family (Cucurbitaceae):
Cantaloupe, cucumber, gourd, kalabasa, honeydew, luffa, pumpkin, squash, watermelon

Potato family (Solanaceae):
Potatoes, Tomatoes, Aubergines and Peppers

Kalabasa is a favorite sweet pumpkin squash that grows well over the perennial peanut.

Sweet corn grown organically and freshly picked is one of the rewards of all our hard work. I eat it raw out in the field as a snack.

Sweet basil is a favorite herb for the restaurants. We enjoy using it in our fresh pesto for pasta dishes and bread.

Various nitrogen-fixing bacteria live on the roots of plants. These bacteria then increase fertility with free atmospheric nitrogen that builds up the soil economically.

8. Legume Usage

L egume usage is *Fundamental #2.* It helps nitrogen fixation. Rotate a legume through every year to add free nitrogen to your system. This is one of the biggest expenses in chemical based agriculture and can be minimized and even replaced by biological practices.

Bacteria help the farmer by adding surplus nitrogen for the next crop. These microbes find the nitrogen in the air and soil, and then they capture [fix] it in small colonies on the roots of the peanut, soybean, pole beans, sitao, etc. The colonies can be seen on the root in small nodules.

Generally referred to as rhizobium, these silent workers of the underworld come in thousands of varieties. They need to be present to maximize your legume production and leave a surplus of fuel for future plantings. Good seed suppliers sell or include the inoculants with your seed order.

If you can't get an inoculant, then stick to what your area grows well. The spores will travel some and over time you will see good nodulation, which indicates a plentiful supply of the rhizoboam. You can propagate the nitrogen-fixing bacteria by taking roots with populations of what you need and steeping them in water and molasses 24 hrs. Then use the drench to soak your seed or spray into the soil with EME after you plant. Once you grow your first patch of peanuts, soybean etc. you can usually keep the colony productive in your future rotations of that legume.

We use 3 types of legumes. Vegetable legumes like pole beans, bush beans, red beans or black beans are good staples. Lentils and mongo, or mung bean are great too. Mung bean grows fast and is a great green fertilizer as well. The perennial peanut is excellent as a cover crop or under sown with maize and papaya. Called mani-mani in the Philippines, *Arachis pintoi* is good as a living mulch, forage and pasture crop in warm climates. Like ordinary peanuts or groundnuts, they are drought tolerant to some degree. During our pronounced dry season, they thin out and go dormant. When the rains return in monsoon season they grow out rich and green surprisingly fast. They can be plowed in as a green manure also. These are all classified as vegetable legumes. They grow an entire life cycle in one year or less so we can call them annuals. Most are very fast growing and produce a high volume of biomass for feed or compost.

We expand small plots section by section. Here you can view 3 stages. After soil preparation (foreground), we plant peanuts. Below that, you can see the corn marching up the hill, a natural choice for following a legume.

There is another group I label shrub legumes. Used as hedgerows and border crops, these incredible plants are longer-term soil stabilizers. They prevent soil erosion when planted across a sloping field. Sometimes called SALT hedges (Sloping Agricultural Land Technology), these perennials fix nitrogen and enrich the soil by cycling nutrients from deep below. The roots are deep and bring up trace elements from sub-soil layers and make the leaves excellent for compost, mulch, a green fertilizer or feedstock. Our goats and hogs love these trimmings in their fermented feeds. We use the rensonii as a cut and carry forage for the goats. They can graze the hedges also. Another hedge that we use successfully is Flemingia. The rensonii propagate from cuttings or seed. Flemingia grows best direct seeded during rainy season or started in the nursery. They attract the nitrogen-fixing bacteria eventually but can be inoculated from existing plants.

Nodules of nitrogen fixing bacteria live on the roots of legumes.

Rensonii is part of the S.A.L.T farming system. Our worker is harvesting "cut and carry" feed for the milking goat and her kids. The shrubs can be kept low but they will grow up to 3 meters high and go to seed. We keep them at 1-2 meters.

Flemingia produces 2 seeds in each pod. When ripe, the pod turns dark brown. The seed is black.

Finally, the third type of legume we plant is the legume tree. Most of the trees here with pods are legumes. Now you have an entire root system from massive trees fixing nitrogen in the soil and producing high protein feed and fertilizer from the vegetative growth. You can use these trees as windbreaks and borders, or prune them back and treat them like hedges and add them to your S.A.L.T. project. If you keep them cut back they still do quite well.

Acacia, Kakawati (Madre de cacao), ipil-ipil, and fire trees are a few examples of legume trees that do well here in the tropics. The key to legume use is to allow natural processes to produce the fertility that you need to succeed. Nutrient cycling is enhanced because minerals and trace elements are brought up from deep below, where vegetable roots would not normally benefit. The trees mine this fertility from down under and release it through composting and livestock wastes that are returned to the topsoil.

Nitrogen fixing bacteria colonies are symbiotic and make a surplus of nitrogen for the next crop.

Kakawati (also called Madre de cacao) is a hardy legume tree that grows from cuttings. It is famous for it's usage as posts that form a living fence.

Neem tree blossoms produce a green seed that turns red when it ripens. Not a legume, the *Azadirachta Indica* is a good companion plant in the salt hedge system with legumes.

Kakawati (or Madre de cacao) is *Gliricidia sepium,* as viewed up close, has an amazing leaf design. Cows, goats, pigs and even chickens eat this high nitrogen legume tree. The leaves are used as a fertilizer to enhance small vegetable beds in the tropics.

Rensonii seed spreads slowly and germinates during rainy season at a very high rate. It needs constant pruning. The leaves are rounder than the pointy leaves of the Flemingia.

Fire trees are legumes that provide shade and feed livestock.

Companion planting is very helpful for pest protection as well as fertility enhancement. Corn under sown to the mongo bean or the Brazilian perennial peanut makes for good yields. Jojo Demafelis inspects the lower canopy and mulch with the author.

9. Companion Planting

Companion planting is _Fundamental #3_. It is also called inter cropping. These crops are used for insect control, to make wind blocks, and they promote soil conservation. When harvested, they are used for compost and feed for livestock. Companion plants also create a desirable mulch and green fertilizer. Under sowing is a very popular means of companion planting also.

Some plants give benefits that help others grow. Tomatoes do well with carrots because the carrots stimulate the growth of tomatoes. Others, like marigold, ward off certain insects. Onions prevent the carrot fly from infesting the root with eggs. Papaya wards off corn pests.

S.A.L.T. hedges [Sloping Agricultural Land Technology] prevent high winds from damaging crops that are planted between rows and filter the wind while preventing erosion. The hedges that make good companions in our system are usually legumes, but any plant can work. Plant rows following the contour of the land and make every other row a different crop. Use the hedge trimmings as mulch, animal feed, compost or green fertilizer. See appendix 1 for more information.

There is a huge range of opinions on which plants help or hurt each other. Some of the results are not always worth the effort, but I included some combinations that work for us. Sharp eyes and good notes help you learn what is going to work on your soil and climate with the crops you decide to grow.

Mixed flowers do well. The perennial peanut, with its yellow flower, is an excellent legume that fertilizes the Vietnamese rose.

According to Advanced Home Gardening by Miranda Smith, dill attracts small beneficials, but inhibits carrot. Mexican bean beetles won't be a pest when you plant petunia with beans. Bush beans inhibit onions but are good with carrots, cauliflower, beets, cucumbers, and cabbage. Some work remarkably well, while others are only seasonal solutions.

Broccoli and cabbage are commonly planted with celery, chamomile, sage, beets, onions, and potatoes. Onions repel the carrot fly, so onions and carrots grow well together. Fennel inhibits many species of plants and has no companions. Plant it alone.

Garlic repels aphids. Nematodes won't wreak havoc when there are lots of marigolds. Marigolds are our favorite weeds now.

Marigold companion planted with perennial peanut and ampalaya.

Small Beneficials are attracted to parsley; Miranda recommends that you interplant with carrot or rose. Some companions hinder other plants. Sunflowers inhibit nitrogen-fixing bacteria.

Chives can protect your roses from aphids. Potato beetle can be controlled by planting eggplant near beans.

All the intercrop guides boast that Stinging Nettle will attract small beneficials. They claim almost all plants benefit from it. We don't have it here in the Philippines but it is a North American weed.

Here are a few suggestions from the Philippines. In *Practical Guide To Organic Gardening* by Pedro D. Sangatanan & Rone L. Sangatanan, they recommend celery with cabbage to protect from the cabbage butterfly. Garlic among your tomatoes and potatoes will prevent blight. Marigolds with beans repel the bean beetle. Radishes with cucumber minimize damage from the cucumber beetle.

At Aloha House we have stumbled on some of the most effective companions by mistake. One time we planted broccoli among some sweet basil seedlings just to use up the space (that alone is a good reason to inter crop), and found total protection from the caterpillar that would usually destroy broccoli when un-netted.

Papaya wards off some of the borers in sweet corn so we started planting lots of them. Papaya trees are all over the place. We have enough for all the babies in the orphanage and we never tire of this great fruit! We now under sow it with a legume like mongo bean or perennial peanuts and it really benefits from the free fertilizer these powerful legumes produce in the root zone.

Asparagus shades ginger as a companion in loose friable soil.

There are many different combinations out there. Just keep researching what will help your crops and keep good records of what is planted so that you can track your progress. Companion planting works well because we increase the bio-diversity of our plants. Composting increases microbial diversity in soil. We will study it next.

Compost is one of the major future sources of fertility for all your food production. A successful operation is always processing crop residue, weeds and manures for anticipated needs. The energy invested is worth its weight in gold. Our guys turn the compost manually with shovels to bring in air and accelerate the process.

10. Composting

Composting is *Fundamental #4*. Compost will build up organic matter and create humus for your soil. The finished product of decomposition is called compost. Composting is a controlled process in which we capture a high percentage of nutrients from our crop residue and return it back to the soil in a form that is very nutritious. Composting is as much an art as a science by which we create an environment for the natural processes of nature to work efficiently. Remember, we feed the soil, and the soil will feed the plant! We will discuss the classic aerobic systems that work well for us. Then we will highlight our anaerobic processes and incorporate them with planting. We also have a very successful Vermiculture operation we will outline for you.

AEROBIC COMPOST

Most aerobic composting methods utilize the heat process from thermophilic bacteria to kill off both pathogens and weed seeds. Carbon-to-nitrogen ratios need to be 30 parts carbon to 1 part nitrogen for best results. The ratio is usually denoted as 30:1 or simply 30, meaning the units of carbon related to one unit of nitrogen. The best compost piles are made in layers. We layer the organic matter. Layering assures that the ratio of ingredients from each class of organic material is balanced. This allows us to see the amounts and proportions that are going into a batch easily. Balanced nutrients are important for high quality production.

Layering assures the proper proportion of carbon and nitrogen for fuel to grow the microbes. The layered pile gets turned 5-7 days after assembly, a total of three times in 3 weeks.

A crude formula by volume would be: 2 sacks of high carbon matter for each sack of high nitrogen ingredient. When we accumulate approximately 1-2 meter^3 of crop residue and weeds we have enough volume to mix. Smaller piles will loose moisture and not hold heat. Piles higher than 2 meter will compress, run out of oxygen quickly and putrefy in the center. You can form a *windrow* as long as you want, but it should not be more than 2 meter high and 2 meter wide. We add 2 pails of bokashi, 2 pails of soil and 10 pails of manure to the crop residue. The soil is helpful in forming humus and bringing in mineral nutrients as well as microorganisms. We add moisture with a hose to get the water content higher. We want it moist but not dripping wet. If we use dry straw or manure we add more water than when starting with wet ingredients. We also add fermented rice wash. This brings in the EM family to insure high quality finished compost.

Compost tumblers make it easier to produce small batches of compost. Composting bacteria need air. It is very easy to aerate compost by rotating the drum. Our steel compost tumbler worked well, but the humic acids are hard on the metal and the welds. The effect is to feed the thermophilic bacteria with oxygen so that they continue to work.

We usually turn piles once every 5-7 days for a total of 3 times to add oxygen. You can vent with air tubes, but mixing/turning is required for best results. The outer layer does not compost till it is in the center and goes through the heat cycle to kill the destructive bacteria. All manure should be composted if used on food crops. The thermophiles work to eliminate pathogens, after 3 turnings they are done working, now the pile will cool. That's 15-21 days for our 3 turnings. Then we let the mesophiles bacteria finish it off at lower temperatures and mature for another 1-2 months. These bacteria dominate at temperatures lower than thermophiles.

A plastic drum lasts longer than steel. It works to aerate the compost by rotating organic matter through the tumbling action of the paddles.

There is much debate over how often it should be turned and how long it needs to mature, but we keep it simple. We use Effective Microorganisms (EM1) to inoculate the pile and guide it away from disease propagation. We use EM in the form of Bokashi. It is high in nitrogen and rich in beneficial bacterial growth.

The forage chopper is an inexpensive alternative for a powered shredding machine. We use ours for chopping corn stalks, sugar cane, weeds, sorghum stalks, etc. The chopped greens make great feed for the goats, hogs and cow. It is ideal for most small scale composting because it increases surface area and gives the microbes more to break down into fertilizer. This one fits onto a metal horse that we use for repairing vehicles. You can make it to stand alone with wooden legs, as long as it is sturdy enough for the constant striking of the mighty bolo (machete).

With the full range of the EM family active in our piles, we find that we can use our compost as fertilizer in 2-3 months. This is the tropics after all; things progress quickly in our Palawan climate. Our microbes set records because there is no fall, winter or spring. The tropical climate also means you can see 3-4 plantings instead of 1-2 in regions where the winters do not permit continual food production.

The microbes keep working; we keep composting. Moreover, we keep planting year round too!

Table 4 - Carbon to Nitrogen [C / N] Ratios

Material	C/N
Chicken Manure	16:1
Hog Manure	19:1
Cow Manure	30:1
Kitchen Waste	20:1
Rice Hull	400:1
Straw	200:1
Saw Dust	300:1

To speed up the composting process, a shredder/chipper is useful. It needs to be able to create surface area efficiently, so that microbes have lots of food. In the tropics it is important to be able to shred coconut and chip branches. Materials become valuable compost in less time when the surface area is increased through shredding, chipping or crushing. Look for good safety features to protect the operators from harm.

ANAEROBIC COMPOSTING

Anaerobic composting is a very efficient process of mixing beneficial microorganisms into materials to create powerful, yet inexpensive fertilizers. This process prevents the heat cycle and preserves energy. It is a more powerful finished product than aerobic compost because material is not decayed but rather fermented (pickled). It finishes decomposing when we mix it into the soil and allow more time for the microbes to do their job. They work very fast compared to classic aerobic style composting and preserve more fertilizer value by eliminating heat and gases.

We make our bokashi with this process. This is one method of anaerobic composting. Bokashi is the Japanese word for fermented plant matter. We mix 1 sack of copra meal to three sacks of low-grade rice bran (D3-gaspang) and three sacks of charcoal. We charcoalize rice hull (D4) in a specialized process ahead of time. These ingredients are mixed dry with shovels on a cement floor.

Bokashi Economy 101 - The foolish American farmer on the right spent 1000 pesos on one sack of complete fertilizer and has no money for seeds. The wise Filipino farmers on the left made a ½ ton of bokashi and have money left over for certified seeds.

Then we pour an EM solution into the mixed grains and waste material. We use 200 ml. of EME and 200 ml. molasses diluted in 10 liters of water to make the solution. We add additional water depending on how dry the materials are. If we substitute manure for copra meal, the moisture is higher and we don't need as much water. However, the target is 40-50% moisture content. You get a feel for it after a while. We do the squeeze test. Just take a handful of your moist bokashi and squeeze it. If it crumbles in your hand after you release it, add more water. It should stick together without dripping when squeezed. This moisture will help fuel the fermentation process and prepare the ingredients for fertilizer use. It doesn't change form till it is buried in the soil.

Bokashi is a great soil conditioner and works well for side dressing. We also lay it on the surface before we mulch. It's a good nitrogen source when properly made. For field applications we make it with rice hull and cow manure. It's important to keep the C/N at around 30:1.

There are quite a few variations. Once you know what you are doing, try using the waste from your area. Use the waste that is economical. We have a bakery nearby with a continual supply of eggshells and ash. The coconut oil factory uses a heat extraction process to draw oil from the dried meat of the nut (copra). They sell this high nitrogen waste product; it makes great feed and excellent fertilizer. Grain mills put out a huge volume of waste products sorted into different grades.

Costing for Aloha Bokashi
(The deluxe copra meal version)

1 sack Copra meal	P	250.00
3 sacks D3	P	90.00
3 sacks RHC	P	90.00
EM & Molasses	P	5.00
TOTAL	P	435.00

This mix will yield 500L of high-grade fertilizer and it is pre-inoculated with EM; containing macronutrients, trace elements, minerals, bulking agents, and soil conditioning organic matter. That's 7 sacks of fertilizer, or P75.00 per sack. So what would you rather have for P1,000.00 pesos, 16 sacks of soil building bokashi or 1 sack of complete fertilizer?

09/05/2005

Bokashi ferments kitchen waste and makes powerful fertilizer. It will ferment for 2 weeks.

At the orphanage we add the copra meal bokashi to our kitchen garbage and see great results. We buy the white 20-liter pails from

Dunkin donuts. We use one kilo of bokashi per 20-liter pail. We add the bokashi to the bottom of the pail to insure smooth fermentation. Then we add our kitchen wastes; things like peelings, bones, cooked food and old rice, layer by layer with the bokashi. We mix each layer of food waste with a stick. The key is to recycle at source. Set it up right in your kitchen. This allows the whole family to participate in the fun of creating your own fertilizers for producing your own vegetables or fruits. The results are worth the effort.

We pack it tight to keep out the oxygen. Anaerobic composting is always without air. This permits the lactic acid forming bacteria to go to work eliminating diseases. When the plastic container is full, just seal it up. It will remain airtight! We place it in the shade for 2 weeks. A label with the date is helpful.

Pour the fermented waste into a hole where you will plant your seed or transfer your seedling. Wait 2 weeks, and then transplant your seedling.

This container will not discharge liquids or cause odors because it is leak proof and air proof. This is the first stage in anaerobic composting and it takes two weeks. Bury the fermented kitchen garbage in the soil. Mix some of the soil that you removed from the hole with the waste. This will assure decomposition within 2 weeks. Therefore, the full process takes only 1 month and it is ready to plant into. No wasted energy from methane gases/foul odors.

Mix with soil and cover for 2 weeks of decomposition then plant on top.

Because you bury it in the soil, it finishes decomposing without rotting or heating up. For large plants or tree seedlings, we dig a single hole, 30 liters in volume, and add our 20-liter pail of fermented kitchen garbage mixed into the soil from the hole we just dug. Make sure the top layer is pure soil so that you do not attract vermin. After 2 weeks the compost is finished. No turning. No fuss. Now you are ready to plant in it. This is a simple system for beginners if you can buy the bokashi from your EM dealer.

There must be phototropic bacteria (Rhodobactor sp.) to maximize the process and also prevent putrefaction (that's when pathogens dominate and cause a foul rotten smell). Lactic acid forming bacteria will biologically exclude or eliminate the pathogens through competitive exclusion. They out eat the bad guys. They starve them.

Our complete "at source" recycling system makes for profitable agriculture and a cleaner future. We capture all our household and farm resources and then utilize them. It turns waste into wonderful products.

These bacteria also break the dormancy of seeds, germinating them before they are in an oxygen environment. This prevents them from becoming weeds. Therefore, instead of expending heat to kill bacteria and seeds, the EM mixture will do it's job without taking energy away from the finished product. This is *synergistic*, synthesizing energy through productive processes that increase the productivity of a system. It keeps the fertility in the compost without spending as much energy as aerobic composting.

We were able to harvest 200 kilos of papaya the first year; we used just 1 pail of fermented kitchen compost! The cost was P6 for 1 kilo of home made bokashi. Using our revolutionary papaya production system, we get 4-5 years from a tree and up to 1 ton of papaya fruits per tree.

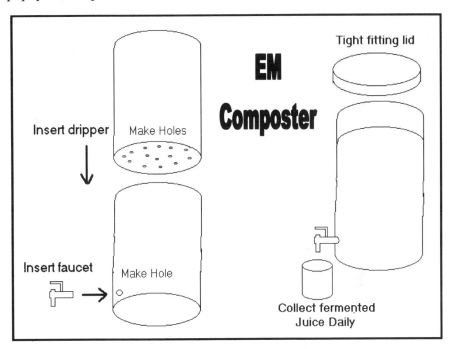

Make your own composter for fermenting kitchen waste

You can collect a liquid fertilizer with the two-container system. Use the bokashi on each layer of food waste and mix with a stick. Then pack it tight to keep out air. When the plastic container is full, place in the shade for 2 weeks. A label with the date is helpful. Remove the liquid through the faucet daily and use in the soil as a fertilizer. It will also clean your septic tank, drains or canals if you pour it down the drain. This liquid extract can be useful as a liquid fertilizer for potted plants and added to the watering system of various drip line schemes. It will add nutrients to the soil and bring the food down through the ground to the plant's root zone for efficient feeding. Use the garbage after 2 weeks like the previous method we discussed.

This is an incredible technology for entire municipalities. They can eliminate organic waste from the landfill. Cities can start programs at the school level. We have an entire curriculum for teaching it in the schools from the BOKASHI USA Network. Teach the young people and they will help implement it at the household level. You could pick a pilot project area and grow as you gain experience. Students learn to use microbial technology for home and commercial applications.

VERMICULTURE

When compost and organic matter is fed to "manure" worms they turn it into a more powerful end product called vermicast. It is in a form that is bio available, rich in beneficial microbial activity, and readily utilized by plants. When your feedstock is not pre-composted, it takes longer for the worms to eat it and may attract ants, mice and rats as well as cause odors. Make sure to use a broad spectrum of organic matter to keep the worm population healthy.

Vermiculture is part of our advanced training, as it requires specialized management, a hands-on portion, and detailed information. Nevertheless, the main points are as follows: of utmost importance are air (oxygen), moisture, bedding and feedstock. The bed is 18" deep and varies in sizes from 3X3 ft. to 4X8 ft.

Composted crop residue is excellent feedstock for your worms.

My wife's natural beauty competes with the beauty of 200 kilos of papaya on one tree.

Papaya grow well in vermicasts, but you need the right worm. There are many varieties of worms, but two main groups: soil workers and composters. You want to use the composters in a vermiculture project that produces natural fertilizer. They flourish horizontally, on the surface, in high concentrations of organic waste.

A proud farmer holds up a harvest grown in our vermicast potting soils. She is the potting soil queen at Aloha House.

The soil workers live vertically in burrows, needing a high soil environment. They are very helpful in the garden and farm, aerating soil increasing the drainage and fertilizing plants. You want to encourage them in your soil, see the chapter on minimal tillage for more tips on utilizing this resource. However, they will die in your worm farm. In our system we use African night crawlers, an excellent manure worm. I've gathered water buffalo dung in the pasture and propagated the manure worm resident to the Philippines; it took longer than the imports, but is an alternative.

The vermi-condos at Aloha House are integrated into the flow of the garden and farm. The kitchen waste comes from above and the vermicasts are harvested and transferred down the hill to the nursery.

We top harvest the casts every week from the surface of the bed. This yields a pure fertilizer without our having to hand sort the worms or screen out the finished product. Humans live above their waste; worms live below it. They travel to the surface and leave behind some of God's best natural fertilizer. We use it for our potting mix. We get about 2-3 inches (10-15 cm) from the surface if everything is properly managed. Our yield is based on the surface area of the bed, depth does not significantly increase yield. The deeper the bed, the more compact it gets, and this can lessen the activity from your crawling friends down below.

With 1 liter of vermicasts per square foot per week you can start to see the size of the project. That might help you estimate your area requirement for the amount of vermicast you set as a goal to meet your nursery needs.

We have 10 beds totaling 151 square feet. Our weekly yield averages 8 pails (times 20 L/pail), or 160 Liters. We harvest 1 liter per square foot per week!

Sign up for an internship and you can learn how to manage your own vermiculture. You will be able to transfer valuable experience to your project. Learn by taking care of an established operation.

Technically, *vermicasts* are the pure fertilizer from the worms. *Vermi-compost* is usually an undisclosed mixture of livestock manure, worm bedding and vermicasts. If you buy vermi-compost you are not getting your money's worth. Some unscrupulous dealers prematurely run their vermi-compost through a screen when the worms have processed about 30% of the feedstock and bedding. That means your buying 70% glorified cow manure at inflated prices. Buy only vermicasts from trusted growers. Better yet, make your own.

After our weekly harvest we use a garden fork to insert air without turning the bedding. This minimizes compaction and keeps the worms active without disturbing them too much. We also insert some carrot fiber from our daily juicing habit. Each day we add the 2-3 kilos of fine fibers to a different bed. We may also soak this in molasses to encourage breeding if we want to replace the worms we sold that month.

Then we put a thin layer of mulch back over the top to encourage daylight activity. Next, we spray it all down with water to keep the moisture level high, around 50-70% moisture content. The evaporation keeps our worm-bedding cooler, which is important for our tropical setting.

Some worms will actually crawl out and try to live elsewhere when the conditions are bad. If the mulch is too thick the airflow is limited. They will evacuate. Soggy bedding and heat from raw manure will drive them out too. Sometimes in the morning we find dead, dried worms around our beds. That tells us that something is wrong. We examine the bedding, moisture and mulch and quickly adjust before we lose them all.

The bedding is composted animal manure. We use it to cover our feedstock, which consists of 20-liter pails of fermented kitchen garbage. They eat it all eventually, even if you use newspaper or cardboard for bedding. Keep it covered to prevent ants from visiting.

So there you have it. Air, water, feedstock and bedding. Your worm project can complete your fertilizer program and save you pesos! Use the right species of earthworm for the task at hand. What's important is that you do your homework and find a system that works best for your project. Start small, grow into to it as you gain experience and master the practices you need to succeed.

These beds are 3X4 feet and 1 foot deep.

Every week we top harvest the vermicasts to assure the highest quality yield, and then we aerate the bed gently with a garden fork.

A ball valve controls the water flow so that workers can run the sprayers for all the beds at once, without having to open them and manually water.

We seldom disturb these silent workers from below. This photo makes the African night crawler look more glamorous than it actually is. It turns garbage into fertilizer. We grow them to make a high-grade additive for our potting soil.

We tested it at the D.A. (Department of Agriculture). The PH is 6.8, and the 3 macronutrients, NPK, are 1.5-1.4-1.5. It's ideal as a fertilizer or compost because of the trace elements it contains as well as the microbial activity. The tested value is secondary to our purposes.

The end product is profitable to sell and can be made into a foliar fertilizer.

Chili and bell peppers do really well in the vermicasts made from our fermented kitchen garbage. The red chili is packaged and sold to restaurants on our island as well as the one grocery store in town; --they call it a "supermarket". We also have customers drop in for some of our specialty items.

The herb crew fills another order for the local market. We sell Indian coriander, cilantro, sweet basil, lemon basil, Thai basil, Chinese parsley, dill weed, garlic chives, onion chives, 3 chili varieties, celery and lemon grass.

Herbs can be very profitable. Each one requires special study and testing, but it's always rewarding to see it on the store shelf. We wholesale to a store that supplies all the hotels and restaurants that use herbs in their dishes. It's convenient for the chefs to get their menu items all at the same place.

Chinese Parsley grows in a vermicast potting mix. Lettuce starts in 20% vermicast potting mix for 3 weeks; it finishes in our raised beds for 4 weeks.

Commercial vermicast production is taking off in Palawan. PCART has a small operation near Roxas. We even feed some of our worms to livestock to supplement protein requirements.

The mungo bean is famous in the tropics as a green manure. It has maximum biomass in the shortest amount of time. At 30-40 days from planting, it can be incorporated back into the soil to feed the next crop.

11. Green Fertilizers

Green fertilizer is *Fundamental #5*. It feeds the next crop efficiently. As you plow crop residue into the soil it will eventually become humus and fertilizer for following crops. It is a form of composting, in which materials do not need to be transported to a mixing/composting site. You could call it field composting.

Economical on a large-scale, green fertilizers will build up the organic matter in the soil. Many of the professional farmers grow a crop to flowering and plow it under before fruiting. This will maximize the biomass and minimize nutrient and energy loss.

In the first year of renovating cogon grassland we use lots of crop residue and green fertilizers, along with mulching. Our popular fertilizer crops are sorghum, hog corn, mongo bean and peanuts. All of our cover crops become green fertilizers later also.

Mustards and pechay are effective as green fertilizers and they can also clean the soil and prevent or eliminate certain diseases.

I know a farmer who grows mongo bean for 30 days, just as a green fertilizer. He plows it under and then follows it with rice. He uses no other fertilizer. His neighbors are rice farmers also. They grow 2 crops of rice, but my friend grows market vegetables in rotation with other non-rice staples after his first crop of rice. He yields 80% more rice in one crop than his neighbors, and then he uses the rest of his land for high value crops. He comes out even with rice because he has one planting instead of two, and one harvest, not two like his neighbors. He gets 180% the harvest for half the labor, and then cleans up with his high value crops while his competition is waiting for the rice to finish. Green fertilizers in crop rotation can bring better profits compared to conventional chemical farming.

Comparison of Green Fertilizers to Conventional Method

One Hectare	Chemical Fertilizer	Green Fertilizer
Plantings	2 Rice	1 Rice
Fertilizer	2 Applications	1 planting
Pesticide	2 Applications	NONE
Harvest	6 tons	5 tons
Yield- tons/ hectare/harvest	3 ton/hectare	5 ton/hectare
Labor	40 man days	18 man days
Other crops	NONE	3 months of market crops and cereals in rotation

Green fertilizers and natural farming techniques lower labor costs while lowering input expenses.

Kudzu is another favorite legume, usually a weed used for plowing under or composting. Our goats eat this hardy vine and keep it under control.

Mulch is piled on deep to keep moisture in the soil and minimize weeds.

12. Mulching

Mulching is *Fundamental #6*. It will conserve topsoil and moisture, as well as provide fertilizer. When straw or crop residue covers the topsoil, it holds it in place while stopping raindrops from compacting soil. Areas with heavy rain require more plowing.

It also slows down rain run off so that moisture can penetrate down to the roots. Erosion is costing farmers valuable organic matter and trace elements. When you mulch, the rain percolates gently into the soil and goes much deeper than when exposed to wind and rain. In dry climates wind erosion can be worse than rain erosion.

Mulching also prevents soil from splashing onto leaves thereby minimizing many disease problems from pathogenic bacteria in the soil. Tomatoes are especially prone to soil borne viruses from splashed soil.

My favorite reason to mulch is weed suppression. If properly applied, 2-3 inches (10-15cm.) of mulch will keep seeds from poking through till your plants are well established. The time you spend mulching is paid back 3 fold in carefree / weed free productivity.

Mulching is yet another form of field composting, where the earthworms and microbes digest the cellulose and feed the plants that follow. It is a source of many nutrients including nitrogen, however there are a few precautions.

You need to hand broadcast a layer of compost or fertilizer with nitrogen before you mulch. Bokashi is good for this. Don't use chemicals. The bacteria that work on mulch will require nitrogen to balance out the high carbon content of the straw. Always lay down compost before using mulches, otherwise it will "lock up" (monopolize) the nitrogen available to the plant and the plant will turn yellowish and lose productivity. Many farmers have experimented with mulch, only to loose their crop due to this small detail-**always lay down nitrogen before you mulch so your crop does not get stunted.** That's why the 30:1 carbon to nitrogen target is important. Review the section on composting if you can't recall the principle of balanced carbon to nitrogen ratios.

Raised beds with mulch are ready for planting.

Another rule of good mulching, learned through experience, is to keep it away from the stems of the plant. If the mulch contacts the stem, some plants can't prosper. Sometimes slugs from our rice straw will traffic to the new seedling, but only if it is touching. So keep a small area around your plants free of the straw or mulch material.

We use rice hull on our walkways; but woodchips are good too. We even use rice hull in the green house.

Walkway mulching suppresses the weeds and will break down over the coming years. It is useful for adding to the raised beds later. The high carbon materials are aged and will decompose readily once they enter the soil. On vegetable beds we use mainly rice straw. Around our papaya trees and seedlings we use legume straws or leaves. We've used cogon grass successfully. It lasts a long time but could be a fire hazard in the beginning when the oil level in the leaves is high. You have to allow it to slope into the stem so moisture will penetrate down into the soil. Otherwise the water runs off. We've also used sugar cane leaves and weeds of all types. Use what you have; just experiment on small areas if you're not sure what will work. Make sure you are not spreading weed seeds if you're mulching with grasses.

Carrot quality and sweetness are enhanced by the phosphates in straw mulch.

Mulching is also part of the nutrient cycle. It releases trace elements from deep-rooted plants onto the surface of the soil. These nutrients are not usually available in the rhizosphere (root zone). Bacteria and fungi quickly digest surface debris. They are especially adept at consuming and converting organic matter into good smelling rich friable topsoil. All the organic matter will eventually feed your plant. The straw mulch in particular will enhance the sweetness of your carrots, peppers, tomatoes, etc. This has to do with natural chemical processes in the soil that facilitate the process as a result of microbial activities that we are still learning about. Acres USA is a resource you can tap on the Albright Model for balanced nutrient management. The complete balance of all required nutrients operate s within maximum and minimum levels and requires careful regulating.

A walkway covered in rice hull prevents soil from eroding and minimizes mud.

Carbonized Rice Hull, or rice hull charcoal is an exotic potting soil amendment in half the world. It's not so good as mulch. Nevertheless, it is famous for it's soil-conditioning properties. It's a harboring agent for EM. We grind it for our goat, hog and chicken feed mix. We make it open air, in a pile, with no specialized equipment. We start a wood fire and smother it with hulls. It's important to keep it from burning. Then we hose it down and it's ready to use.

Ready to eat off-season watermelon produces high sugar content when we use heavy mulch.

We grow the perennial peanut or mani-mani between raised beds of lettuce, protecting the soil. It's a tropical legume from Brazil.

13. Cover Cropping

C over cropping is _Fundamental #7_. It is the technique of growing plants that protect the soil to conserve topsoil and moisture. It can be considered a living mulch. Under sowing legumes below existing crops and other companion plants will work well. You get all the advantages of mulching; soil conservation, moisture retention, increased microbial activity, etc., but in addition the canopy which covers and protects the soil is living and dynamic.

Camote or sweet potato, Kang Kong and perennial peanuts cover the topsoil and hold it in place while stopping raindrops from compacting soil. We also use alugbati, or Malabar spinach, to slow run off so that it can penetrate deep down. This may eventually be used as forage, grazed, harvested, composted or used as a green fertilizer. Be sure to pull back the cover crop when starting seedlings. Most plants will compete for nutrients and the established canopy usually wins. The perennial peanut grows right up to our papaya trunk without inhibiting it. However, corn, we have found, needs more space around the seeded area to establish itself.

To maximize the power of cover cropping, we had to learn to use legumes such as alfalfa, hairy vetch, clovers and peanut vines. They will add value to the overall system. These are good pioneer crops; we plant them when we are establishing new soil.

Legumes fix nitrogen and increase the fertility of soil. The leaves are high in nitrogen and valuable as feed and fertilizer. All kinds of cover crops have been used, sometimes as a free standing crop, other times under sown to protect soil as the main crop gets established. Cover crops are part of the overall solution to soil management. Minimal tillage is a key to natural soil management. It will be explored later.

Never leave your soil exposed to sun and rain erosion for long periods of time. Even grasses grown as a pasture are a good cover. The manure will enrich the soil and the grass will add fertility while boosting bacterial growth. The roots from grasses usually do not survive the plowing process if EM is sprayed before turning it under. It ferments the roots and creates fertilizer before the grass sprouts again!

Cover crops and vines crawl over the soil and prevent weeds from getting established.

Soybeans and alfalfa are under sown to cover our topsoil.

Alugbati is Malabar spinach. This is a great crop if you rotate it. It crowds out weeds and preserves moisture and soil. It does well as a cover crop because it blankets the ground. I like it because the goats and pigs enjoy it so much. It reduces our feed costs as a "cut and carry" forage crop.

After the first plowing, the beds are mixed with composts, rice hulls, charcoal and green fertilizers. Then mulch is used to cover the new beds. We never plow again.

14. Minimal Tillage

Minimal Tillage is _Fundamental #8_. It will preserve soil life and structure, save labor and increase profits. The soil food web is disturbed when continual plowing is practiced. The hoofs of the carabao (water buffalo) or tractor compact the soil while the plow causes disruption in microorganism activity.

As the soil compacts, a pan develops, where sub soil at the depth of the plow can form a barrier layer that roots cannot penetrate. Then rainwater is kept from penetrating the ground and easily floods. The water is stuck at the upper levels of the soil. So are the earthworms.

Earthworms retreat and are slowed down in feeding and breeding with regular plow activity. It is important to keep the soil healthy with earthworms, but tilling prevents the build up of high populations of these helpful creatures. When the initial plowing is finished we only use hand tools to add rice hull, charcoal and compost into the soil. Here in the tropics, by the second year we are mainly direct seeding, hand drilling and transplanting into mulched beds.

On a small scale, blocks can be stacked to produce a handsome vegetable bed that prevents flooding and keeps soil friable.

The rapidly accumulating topsoil is loose, friable and high in organic matter. Earthworms and roots will promote macro porosity, opening the soil for water absorption and microbial activity.

We use raised beds that are 3 ft. wide. This allows us to reach in without compacting the soil. The more we traffic on the soil, the more compressed it gets. This prevents microbial activity and earthworms are also encumbered by the heavy soil where feet have stepped. Filipinos tend to be just over 5 feet, so a four-foot wide bed causes them to step into the bed and compact the soil.

The raised beds are never walked on. Workers reach into the bed from the side to plant and harvest. This minimizes compaction.

The broad fork is used to put air in the soil without turning it. It is designed to minimize stress to the body while creating great soil. Use the mechanics of your legs and shoulders and save your back.

If you don't turn the soil, microorganisms, insects and worms are not disturbed. They benefit from the added oxygen and keep the soil open and friable. We just keep the soil open with the broad fork. We can do a lot of area in one day with this clever invention.

In the green house we use seedling bags to grow out our tomatoes, bell pepper and our other special crops. We mix specialty soils for filling bags instead of tilling the soil.

The tractor is a big help in turning the soil. We use water buffaloes or tractors the first time, we never need them again. With root activity and low traffic, the soil in our raised beds doesn't become compacted. There are also tractor attachments for aerating the soil without having to turn it.

Even the plowing from your livestock can form a layer of soil below the surface that will cause a pan. The pan causes flooding and prevents roots from going deep into the subsoil.

Vine ripe tomatoes are possible if your insect balance is achieved. You have to allow the predators to find an environment to populate.

15. Insect Habitat

I nsect habitat is *Fundamental #9*. Insects populate and bring stability to your system if you allow the predators and beneficial species a place to live. Plant insect habitat for beneficial species and bait crops for the bad guys.

Many pest problems can be minimized with habitat that promotes predator insects. These environs include hedges and flower gardens because the spiders and pollinators thrive in them. An herb garden is great at attracting helpful insects and repelling some pests. Even strips of specialty plants can be harvested to spread the beneficial insects that take residence in them. Water areas, fountains and streams also bring in insects, toads and frogs, along with birds. A small pond with non-stagnant water will bring in more helpers for your garden. Birds are very helpful in the ecology of your farm. Many bird species eat large quantities of insects every day.

Archie points out a reptile hiding in the Aloe Vera planter. Reptiles can eat a large amount of pests each day or night, depending on sleep patterns.

You can distract certain pests with crops they prefer while growing ones they would not otherwise overlook. Their regular choice will survive with less infestation. We call this bait cropping. It helps in the nursery and green house.

The green house and potting shed are surrounded by natural habitat that promotes predator insects. Butterflies are safe in the natural farm. There are no insecticides or pesticides applied in a genuine natural farm. Never, ever! That allows the insect population to find a niche and maintain a balance.

Cucumbers are hit hard in the tropics by beetles. If you use the right companion plants and allow for predator habitat, you can get some wonderful fruits, free of insecticides. Some crops are best left to the seasons they thrive in.

Pollinators can be encouraged to visit your farm if you don't spray chemicals. You can plant flowers, clovers and fruit trees your localized bees prefer. Colors are a welcome sight in the farm.

Poor soils force the beetle larvae to feed on roots. In healthy soil they eat organic matter and crop damage is minimal.

It is good to attract bees; they will insure better all - around pollination.

An integrated livestock unit provides the small farmer with an excellent source of income while building up his fertilizer reserves.

16. Livestock Integration

The best way to finish off your dream farm or garden is to balance it with a small livestock unit. Animal integration is _Fundamental #10_. It will create a low cost high quality fertilizer source as well as produce food to eat.

Livestock properly managed will bring the tropical farmer higher profits than some market vegetables and most grains. We raise goats, chickens and hogs. Our goats graze and browse as well as feed on fermented grains. Some crop residues are fed to the goats; it reduces feed costs and their manure will reduce fertilizer costs. We cut and carry feed stock fresh while some confined grazing is practiced. Concentrated grains are used as a supplement to pasturage. Grains are fermented with beneficial microbes to increase feed conversion and act as a probiotic, eliminating all medications. The feed creates natural vitamins and health enhancing components that protect livestock because EM is active in it. The cost of the EM is far less than antibiotics and vitamin shots and replaces all antibiotics. Our goat-breeding program been successful; we're expanding it. We are looking for a cow to pasture; we've some premium legumes for grazing.

All pens and barns are sprayed with EM weekly to minimize odors and flies. The pathogens are excluded through competition.

Table 5- EM Economy

EM 1	EM E	Back Pack Sprayer	ml/m^2	Area Sprayed
	30 ml	1	100	150 m^2
30 ml	1 L	33	100	4,950 m^2
1 L	30 L	1,000	100	15 hectares

The economy of EM speaks for itself. One bottle covers a lot. 30 ml. of EM1 makes 1 liter of EM Extended which makes 33 backpack sprayers, which covers ½ hectare or 1.25 Acres. A bottle of EM1, extended and diluted, will cover 15 hectares or 37 acres.

For our cut and carry operation we use a forage cutter to hold the stalks. The goats feed in their house till the sun dries the pasture. Then it is safe to graze. Parasites infect the rumen when grasses are wet.

We feed the bucks, kids and does with rensonii and flemingia leaves as well as 12 other plants and an EM fermented grain supplement made of soy meal, copra meal, cut greens, rice bran, molasses, charcoal, lime and salt. Then they go in the barn with a sawdust floor 1 meter deep.

Archie checks on the kids. They graduated to the bigger barn.

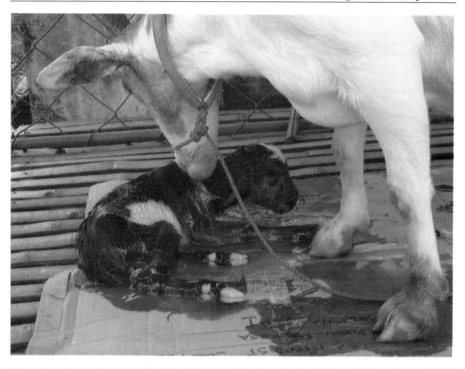

The doe cleans her young after she gives birth. She had three kids and required some extra care, good pasture and fermented feeds.

The kids go out to pasture a few days from birth. They know how to find the milk, but grazing took a few weeks. The children help with shepherding the flock.

The 3 kids had only two utters to fight over, so we gave formula supplements to keep them all growing. Each kid was able to adjust to our supplemental feedings.

The proud buck- This Anglo Nubian is bigger than the native goats and will help us upgrade the herd. This is a good milking breed and will increase the capacity of the local goats while increasing the disease resistance and overall vigor of his offspring.

For hog fattening we feed rice bran, soy and copra meal fermented in EM. Again, crop residue fed to swine lowers feed costs. We use sawdust beddings to minimize stress and allow natural rooting or scratching instincts that can't be practiced on cement. It minimizes the odors and flies too! Our hog fattening has been the most successful; we will add a furrowing unit next. We will detail more of our hog fattening program later in this chapter.

Our free-range-chicken eat corn, sorghum, rice bran, copra meal with fermented EM Bokashi. The layers get crushed limestone as well. They have plenty of habitat to graze and scratch with water always available. The house has a bedding of natural ingredients like the swine bed. However, we use a little rice hull and more charcoal to stabilize the manure. It is very low odor and has minimal flies.

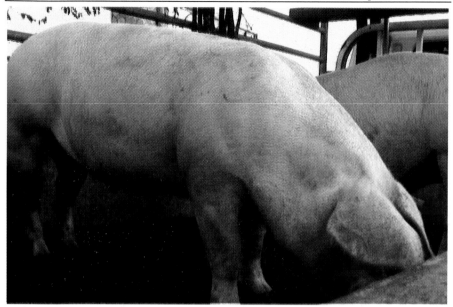

112 Kilo Champions from Erin Nixie Farm- Good breeds will always perform well on good feeds. Our hogs are economical to grow because we make our own feeds and use crop residue to reduce feed costs. The key is to limit them to 1 kilo per day of the costlier grains after they are 70-80 kilos weight.

This is by no means a complete guide for hog raising. We hope to produce a guide that is livestock specific soon. We highlight our hog system merely to display the potential of this technology as we have adapted it from the Korean Natural Farming method.

Fermented Feed- Starter:

Crude Protein 18.16%

	Crude Protein	Weight (Kg)
Rice Bran [D1]	14.00%	50.00
Copra Meal	22.00%	7.00
Soy Meal	47.00%	10.00
Greens	15.00%	15.00
EM & Molasses	100ml ea.	
	/ 10 Liters	

Hog fattening requires attentive care and supervision but leaves most of your day free for vegetable production. Cash cropping or market vegetables grow well in our fermented manures from pigs, cows, and goats.

Vegetative Feed

The following have been used successfully at Aloha House.

Depend on these crop residues to lower feed costs:

Fermenting Greens- Legumes are best, Peanuts, Kakawati (Madre de cacao), Ipil-Ipil, Flemingia, Rensonii, Kudzu
*No Sitao or pole beans, no Cassava leaves.

Snacking Greens- Camote, Kang Kong, Coco leaves, Grasses, clover, Alugbati, Carrot tops, Maize stalks, Peanuts
*No Sitao or pole beans, no Cassava leaves.

Snacking Fruits and Vegetables – Tomato, cucumber, banana, watermelon, papaya, pineapple waste, chopped upo or patola.

Harvest day is when we call our pre-sold customers in for their natural pork. They pay a premium price because it tastes like wild boar. We do not use commercial feeds or fishmeal, so our finished hogs taste better than the commercial product, and are without any dangerous chemical residues.

When our suppliers can deliver, we are able to raise two batches of pigs at once. The weaners are in a smaller pen; the finishers are given 2 sq. meters each. They love the bedding. No need to waste water washing. To assure a better supply of fatteners, we are getting ready for furrowing next.

Bedding of the Pig Pen

Materials Description:

- Sawdust- the coarse or the fine dust, but a mixture will work well.
- Rice Hull Charcoal- Carbonized, not ash [any ground charcoal]
- Soil - Preferably sandy loam or garden soil but clay soil is o.k.
- Salt - Table Salt or rock salt.

Mixture:

Sawdust = 10 Sacks
Sandy Loam = 2 Sacks
    or Clay Soil = 1 Sack
Charcoal = 1 Sack
Salt = ½ kilo

Procedure: Make small batches and layer the components after they are mixed. Make a mixture of 10 sacks sawdust, 1 soil etc. then spread out and mix next batch till you have 3 feet deep.

Spray in EM Extended 1:100, add water to 30% moisture. Continue the process till the 1-meter hole for bedding is filled. The Charcoal is a harboring agent for the microbes; it is important for long-term stability, health and odor control of the bedding. Sea Salt helps provide trace minerals and the soil is actually eaten by the animals. You can also mix Bokashi in each layer at 1-kilo/10 sacks sawdust.

Fattening House for the Pig

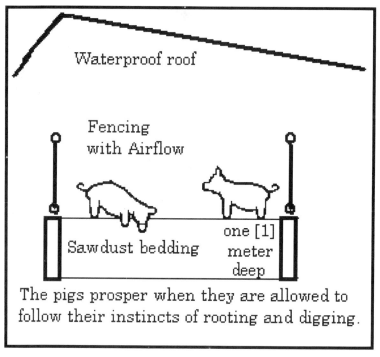

Waterproof roof

Fencing with Airflow

Sawdust bedding

one [1] meter deep

The pigs prosper when they are allowed to follow their instincts of rooting and digging.

Make the roof leak proof with good airflow below. Bedding cannot get wet. You must not build over low areas where water will leach into the bedding. The bedding is one (1) meter deep and lined with hollow block to prevent the pigs from digging under fencing.

We have two designs for the roof; either one works as long as rain does not enter. The hogs need help staying cool and **we no longer spray them or wash them with water.** That's why we have good airflow. Keep them cool and they will eat more and grow bigger, faster. Water would destroy the bedding, attract flies, and produce odors. EME is sprayed weekly on our dry beds to control flies and odors. In addition, drinking water is treated with EME 1:1000 and feed is fermented with EM.

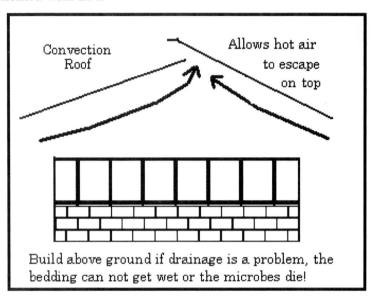

Convection Roof

Allows hot air to escape on top

Build above ground if drainage is a problem, the bedding can not get wet or the microbes die!

TWO [2] SQUARE METERS ARE REQUIRED PER PIG FOR FATTENING; OVER CROWDING DOES NOT WORK. Over crowding means your average weight will be lower and diseases will get an edge. Space is required for your hogs.

Pig Problems

Never feed them sitao or pole beans. These are toxic to pigs. Use ipil-ipil, Kakawati (Madre de cacao) sparingly. Rice hull is not advisable in the bedding. Coco lumber sawdust is best. Gemelina sawdust is BAWAL, toxic to pigs. Bad odor is from wet bedding or bad feed. Do not feed with kitchen/ restaurant food. Do not feed your livestock with low-grade rice bran like darak [D2]- use only Tiki-Tiki

[D1]. Soy meal and copra meal are high protein. 10% copra meal is the maximum in feed; more will cause LBM (diarrhea). Call your vet if problems last more than 5 days.

Trouble Shooting- look at each possible solution as it relates to your problem. Consult a vet if problems persist more than five days.

Table 6- Trouble Shooting

Problem	Possible Cause	Solutions
Foul Odor	Bad feed	Mix without kitchen waste, use soy meal not fish meal
	Wet bedding	Improve dripper drainage, fix roof leaks, house in low area- move out of flood area
	No beneficial microbes	Use EME in bedding, feed and water
Rashes on Pigs	Sitao in feed	Quit feeding sitao; try other legumes
	Too much Kakawati, Ipil-Ipil	Quit feeding Kakawati, Ipil-Ipil
	Rice hull (ipa) in bedding	Use sawdust only
	Mites	Isolate, coat with oil / aloe Vera
Slow Growth	Bad genetics	Get professionally bred hogs
	Bad feed mix	Use high protein feed stock and crop residue
	Not ad lib	First 3 mos. Feed continually daytime
	Stress	Over crowding, give 2 m^2 each pig
Diarrhea	Bad feed	Ferment with EME one week, 10% copra meal only
	Too much soil/shallow bed	Remove soil - Add sawdust
Flies	Wet bedding	Improve dripper drainage, fix roof leaks, house in low area- move out of flood area
	No beneficial microbes	Use EME in bedding, feed and water
	Bad feed	Mix without kitchen waste, use soy meal not fish meal

Calculating the Fertilizer Value of Manure

We average 4-5 cubic meters of manure from 4 months of production with 8 hogs. That amounts to 180 pails [X 20 Liters].

Example: Eight fatteners can produce enough fertilizer for 750 sq. Meters of watermelon. That soil can then produce 120 pcs. of organic watermelon averaging 4 kilos each. Off-season we can earn 20 pesos/kg. That is P8,000.00 gross income from pig manure! Moreover, that's on top of our sales for the meat. This is premium-inoculated fertilizer; we stockpile it and compost it. It's ready in only 2 months.

	Future Expansion	Mixing/ Composting	Future Expansion
8.00	Future Expansion	First Bay (hogs)	Future Expansion

4.00

4.00

Expansion

As success is achieved, expansion can be done in modules. Each bay can fatten 8 hogs and bring a net profit of P1,000.00-2,000.00 per head, with a five bay build out potential of P80,000.00 pesos /quarter. Moreover, the manure from the hogs would be over 25 cubic meters. That could fertilize a hectare of sweet corn and produce another P50,000.00 profit, in addition to your meat sales.

We feed ad lib (continually) till 50 Kilos, then 2 times daily till 70 Kilos. Then, till we bring them to market we give them only 1 Kilo of fermented feeds and the rest is crop residue from the farm 3X/day. This lowers our cost of fattening considerably while creating great fertilizer reserves. The savings are great because they eat an incredible volume with less efficient conversion to weight, no one could afford to raise 110-kilo hogs on commercial feeds.

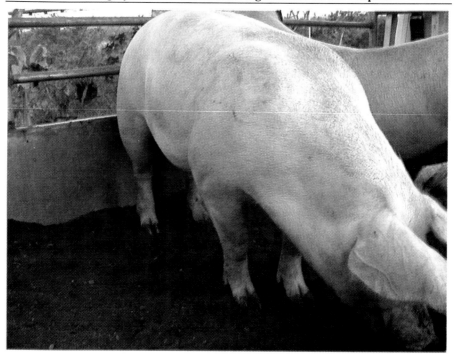

Our farm record was set by this porker at 112 kilos; that's about 250 lbs.; the other one in this batch was 109 kilos.

When we get good stocks from honest growers, we do well. Not all growers are forthright. You have to ask a lot of questions and inspect each animal thoroughly. However, proper management is as important as having the proper breeds. The following batch was our biggest success to date. The Erin Nixie farm supplied us with a few good batches. They breed about 100 sows and fatten also. We need to provide transportation for the piglets to lower their stress and help them in the transition.

Total Weight Kg. (8 heads)	Total gross Income In Pesos	Average Pesos/ Kilo	Total Cost In Pesos	Total Profit In Pesos
738.00	67,508.00	91.47	37,712.00	29,796.00

Our averages for meat sales were very good, and we had plenty of free fertilizer from composted manure for corn! This further lowers fattening costs.

ERIN NIXIE FARM HOG FATTENERS

Average Weight per Hog 92.25 Kg	Average Income per Hog P 3,742.50

Breakdown for Erin Nixie Farm, Binduyan, Palawan. Weaned, Landraise-Large White. Fattened for 4.5 months at Aloha House, Batch 304. Harvested over a four-week period in May 2005.

Age In Months	Live Weight Kilos	Gross Income Pesos	PESOS/ Kilo	Total COST (Piglet P2,500) Pesos	Profit In Pesos
6.0	112	10,335.00	92.28	5,188.00	5,147.00
6.0	108	9,229.00	85.45	5,092.00	4,137.00
5.7	103	9,325.00	90.53	4,972.00	4,353.00
5.7	92	8,200.00	89.13	4,708.00	3,492.00
5.4	86	8,043.00	93.52	4,564.00	3,479.00
5.4	79	7,459.00	94.42	4,396.00	3,063.00
5.0	80	7,542.00	94.28	4,420.00	3,122.00
5.0	78	7,375.00	94.55	4,372.00	3,003.00

Good breeds with good genetics are of utmost importance. Good breeds with bad genetics won't perform, and bad feed will stunt the best of genes. The beginning protein levels can't be compromised. We are able to finish these animals at 6 months because we are giving them only 1 kilo of our own feed, and the rest is free crop residue from our various legumes and vegetables. We started butchering this batch at 5 months, the smallest first. We were really surprised by the time we did the last batch. The meat was still tender at 6 months old and tasted like wild pork. Commercial growers can't afford to finish hogs to this weight because of the cost of their feeds.

The only problem we have with this system is getting a big enough truck to move these guys off to the market. We keep our fattening costs low because we give them only 1 kilo of fermented feeds at 70-80 kilos and finish them with crop residue.

Phase Out Feeding Schedule

Week	Commercial Feed	Fermented Feed
1	75%	25%
2	50%	50%
3	25%	75%
4	0%	100%

We transition our piglets from toxic commercial feeds. Piglets usually get diarrhea during the second week. Give them bananas and ground charcoal in their fermented feeds. It's much easier to convert young animals to the natural system. Old sows are high risk to convert. Always call a veterinarian when problems persist more than 4-6 days.

EM treatments are used successfully for horses and water buffalo.

"At source" recycling means doing your job at home and not relying on the government to solve your trash problems. It has value to your farm.

17. Resource Recovery Tour

Unused resources are called waste. If you use the waste in your compost, you turn it into fertilizer. It's no longer waste, right? There's no longer any need to have organic waste filling our landfill. We can use all of it in our system. For our purposes the opposite of waste would be useful. Call it useful, don't call it waste. We ferment our kitchen waste and it becomes useful. Use your useful materials in the garden!

As a matter of fact, most homes have 10-12 different waste categories. Then there are industrial classes of waste, commercial waste, and agricultural waste. These are all resources you can recover. resources that add fertility to your overall program and bring about economic and environmental success. If you study our chart below you might get some ideas for your home, office, farm or school.

Aloha House Inc Resource Recovery

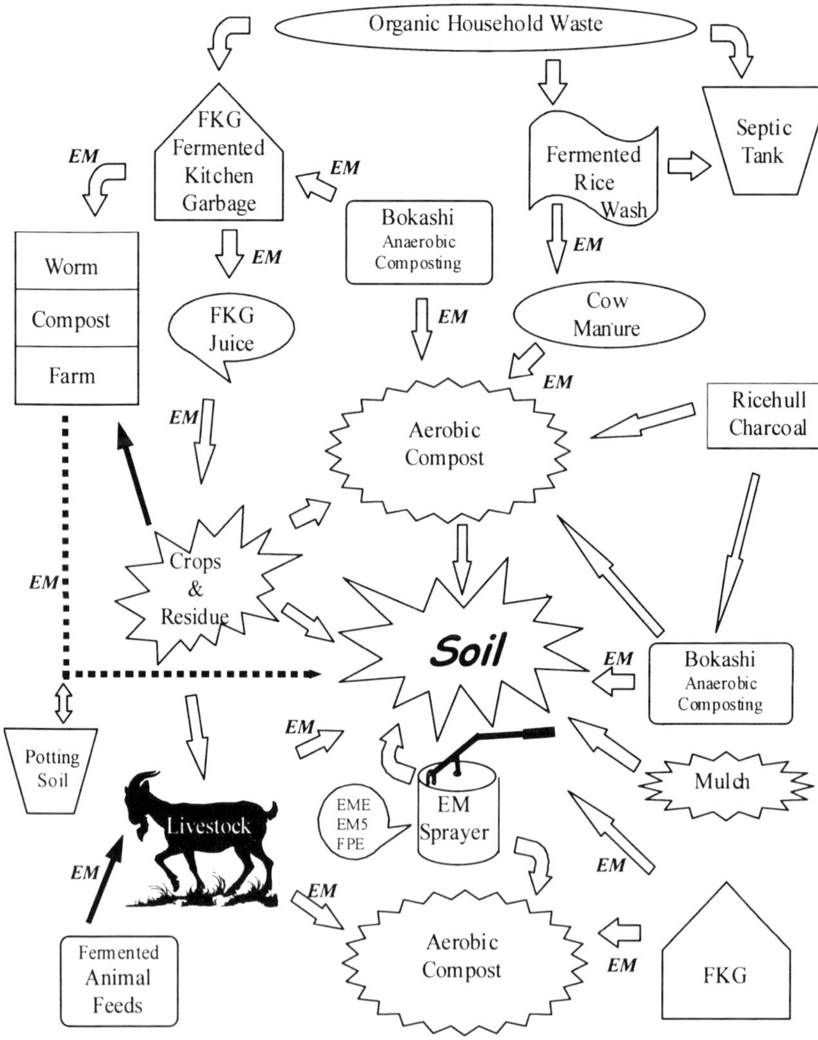

Notice that everything is working its way back to the soil. That is the goal after all - feed the soil and it will feed the plant. Through microbial action and insect activity, the nutrients from your waste become fertilizers.

We didn't get to this point over night. We added each component one at a time till we were able to achieve the tasks we set as goals. For example, from my research results, I saw vermiculture as an obvious priority for us, because of the high volume of kitchen waste we generate at the orphanage. First, we learned to make bokashi, and then we used it in field applications. Then we treated our food waste. When it finished fermenting, we planted in some of it and fed the rest to our worms. Now we use the vermicasts in our potting soil for our nursery. Each step was birthed and meticulously micromanaged till the staff mastered each level and task.

Photo copy this page and cut out the shapes that will help you make a flowchart. Arrange according to priority and workflow, then major routes.

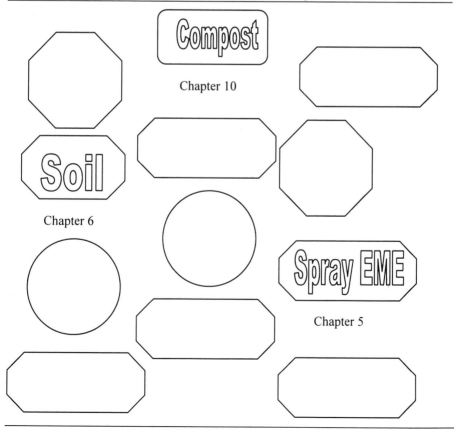

Compost

Chapter 10

Soil

Chapter 6

Spray EME

Chapter 5

Wheelbarrows and trucks will need access to your project; provide alternative routes and roadways for the future.

18. Planning Session

Plans should be drawn up before any effort is wasted. Think through your traffic routes and flow of materials. Integrate your resource recovery plan in this process. Set your goals and lay down the steps that you think are needed as you see it now. Write it down; it will be a flexible starting point. Even the best laid plans can fail, but remember, you are gathering data from your experience and can progress even when you make a mistake or are broadsided by unforeseen circumstances.

The following is our step-by-step guide to getting started with Natural Farming, including an EM Usage Plan. Each step should be streamlined before you add another. You should be able to master the basics first, and then go on to the more complex. You are building a foundation; make sure it is on solid rock, not shifting sand. From number 4 the order is not important. Just make sure you are on top of it each step of the way.

Farm Layout and Flow of Materials

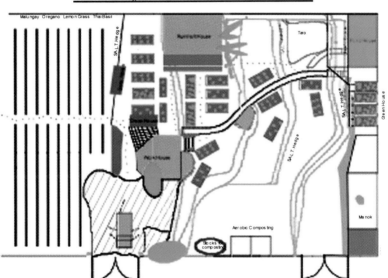

Sample Farm Layout-Aloha House, Mitra Rd., Santa Monica, Puerto Princesa City, Palawan, PHILIPPINES.

Flow of Materials

1. Identify Resources – Plan with low cost inputs and efficient processing to keep your start up and operation costs low.

- Finalize Resource Recovery system

- Make a Farm Layout

- Plan Materials Route

- Centralize Composting Area

- Identify Wastes for fertilizers. Bakery = Eggs, Oil Factory = Copra meal, Rice or wheat Mill = Bran, Farm = Straw, Rice Wash and household waste, restaurant waste, municipal waste, neighborhood grass cuttings...

2. List all the plants you want to produce. It's helpful to know how you will plant everything you want. We recommend mastering 2 new plants at a time. Once you succeed in meeting their needs, add 2 more. It is wise to grow what you are already buying; this is the most economical way to "sell" your product. You are replacing your store - bought, low-quality, retail produce at below wholesale prices. It's way fresher and more nutritious! That's the best return you will ever get. Then grow a surplus for sale at market prices.

3. Utilize EME, Bokashi, vermicasts, bat guano, lime, and make potting soil from samples kit in seminar.

4. Buy your own EM1 and extend EM1 to save money.

5. Make Fermented Rice Wash – 5ml EM1: 5ml. Molasses: 1 liter rice wash. It makes a good soil spray and compost activator. It also can treat plants at 1:1:500.

6. Make Bokashi- use your EME to ferment wheat bran or rice bran [Magaspang (grade D3) from the mill.]

7. Make Fermented Kitchen Garbage – Garbage is a good fertilizer if properly inoculated. The EM is in your bokashi; this will ferment the kitchen/food waste.

8. Make EM5 spray instead of EME. Now you are an advanced EM user and your farm will be progressing for years to come.

9. Make FPE – Fermented Plant Extracts are explained in Appendix 5. These capture nutrients from weeds and multiply microbes.

10. Make ACT (Aerated Compost Tea) from high quality vermicasts or aerobic compost. Spray the bacteria and fungi regularly. Run an aquarium pump for 12-36 hours with close monitoring. Vermicasts make some of the best tea known to modern science. The longer the brew the higher the fungal count, but the bacterial growth starts to diminish over time. Brew high numbers of fungi for perennials; high bacterial counts are best for annuals like market vegetables and rice.

Foliar sprays will not harm your pollinators and helps herbs like mint, basil and Indian coriander.

Interns get to learn through doing. They also see the complete crop cycle - from planting to harvest. We require a four-month minimum.

19. Internships

The real hands on school of success is to intern with a working farm. Then you can learn first hand from experience. You will appreciate the land, soil and even the process of efficient food production more.

The special relationship we enter into with the land is called Husbandry. You've heard of animal husbandry, but land requires stewardship that is very unique compared to that required by your other possessions. We are married to the land in one sense. We are to take care of it for generations to come. Short-sited profiteering with environmental abuse proves that the owner is a pimp, not a husband.

When the land is treated like a prostitute, it goes through many abusive relationships.

Community organizing and social work is handled by Aloha House Staff. Annacar is our licensed social worker. She helps organize families for training, counseling and financial assistance.

We teach the stewardship that each person has during our internship program. They learn more than just technique; they get to see the big picture. We were created by an all-wise and perfect Creator. He gives us opportunity to serve Him. We can learn to till the land and better care for this planet. Our interns can learn value in providing quality food in a sustainable operation.

Why not watch over your land with the intention of permanently preserving it for generations to come, like the way a good husband looks after his wife, loving and caring for her while working together toward common goals. Teamwork makes a marriage successful, and it is the same with land. Mutual benefits develops between the steward and his land. The relationship creates value over time.

Make your farmland a sanctuary for wildlife, birds and insects by committing to never spraying chemicals. Plant and harvest all you want, but allow the natural balance to develop into a climax vegetative state.

Farmers and cooks harvest the food we need for the orphanage daily; fresh and pesticide free.

Live with some of your wet areas. You don't need to drain all the low-lying places. Learn to grow wild rice or other natural food crops. Avoid diverting waterways with cement and steel. Plant the shoreline with SALT hedges and legume trees, serving a dual purpose. They will keep topsoil in place with sturdy root growth and cycle nutrients for other crops. Plant local species that thrive like berries.

Sugar cane is self-mulching and creates a lot of biomass. This in turn affords earthworms better feed and they can multiply, increasing the fertility of the soil.

We encourage interns to plant indigenous fruit trees. Even root crops can be found native to most area. Don't clear-cut or slash and burn like the shifting cultivators. Stay on your clearing and maintain soil fertility. Build up, don't tear down. Practice renewable forestry, with selective harvesting and sustainable management that allows time for hardwood species or Raton to be replaced.

Every farmer should consider himself married to the land till death. Then he should get buried there and make one last contribution to its fertility! Now his heirs will be able to follow your pattern for generations to come. Land is the most precious heirloom.

Interns learn to cope with the forces of nature. When wind damage from a typhoon knocks down a prized corn stand, the plant has to be reinforced with soil mounds.

Any farmer who wants to develop his techniques should try an internship. It is a time honored tradition in most trades and will be valuable experience. It's training time you will not be able to carve out of your schedule once you have your own project. The methods and practices learned through repetition and day-to-day reality will decrease time wasted on your own farm. Your mistakes will not be as catastrophic in an established farm! When you start without this internship exposure, you will loose a lot of time and money learning the hard way. Why not learn from someone that made the mistakes for you? Learn what they went through and don't repeat their mistakes; make new ones based on insights that will lower your risk. You're sure to fumble in the beginning. We did. However, the lessons learned from previous projects allowed us to progress quickly. We hope our interns will progress quickly too!

Pastor Joseph "Jojo" Demafelis took this picture of a SALT hedge in the mountains of Palawan. He trained a Batak tribe on how to use Sloping Agricultural Land Technology to save their ancestral lands. The thick double rows of flemingia and rensonii follow the contour and capture run off, creating level areas to plant over the coming years.

Appendix 1-S.A.L.T.

Sloping Agricultural Land Technology (SALT) has made steep worthless lands usable. This is a practice valuable to the tribal community. They are learning to stabilize topsoil with the proper selection of species. They can maintain their ancestral lands without having to destroy them through shifting cultivation, otherwise known as slash and burn farming.

I was able to observe this SALT technology while staying with a Christian ministry in Palawan. They trained Christian workers and tribal members to implement the hedge systems for the betterment of the respective tribal groups they were helping. The results were dramatic.

There is a wide family of legume shrubs that prevent erosion and make excellent fertilizer and feed stock. Any farm can find the proper species to plant for any area, (even on flat land as a border crop). On our lot we have implemented various combinations of wind blocks, erosion controls and fodder crops that keep everything in balance. They bring in beneficial insects and bird nests.

Flemingia macrophylla is also called other names.

With a healthy hedge system growing, the soil in the root zone is a breeding center for soil dwelling earthworms that benefit from the lack of tillage. There is no interruption in their life cycle.

Much has been written on this method, but in the tropics Mount Carmel in Davao, Mindanao, Philippines has the most information available. They also sell seeds for the species adapted to this climate. I have been able to utilize both the rensonii and flemingia and now grow my own seed stock for our students.

Flemingia has two seeds in each pod.

Desmodium rensonii is a favorite of our goats. It has small disc like seeds.

S.A.L.T. hedges prevent high winds from damaging crops that are planted between rows and filter the wind while preventing erosion. The trees and small twigs from shrubs also provide fuel for cooking. The hedges that make good companions in our system are usually legumes, but any plant can work. Plant rows following the contour of the land and make every other row a different crop. Keep trimming the plants and use the hedge trimmings as mulch, animal feed, compost or green fertilizer. Acacia auriculiformis and Acacia angustissima are popular fodder crops and can tolerate wetter climates.

Azadirachta indica - Neem trees can be cut back and kept as a shrub. Intercrop them with your legume trees and shrubs. Melia azedarach is the counterfeit neem, called China Berry in the USA. It has some of the properties of neem but is inferior in active ingredients and the limbs are brittle.

Rensonii is deep rooted and brings up nutrients from deep down in the sub-soil levels. Its seeds germinate well when stored properly.

Flamengia seedlings are growing in uniform rows. They will prevent erosion in the coming years and feed many goats.

The Bokashi Barn - Bokashi is ready for field application after we ferment it for 2 weeks. It works well as a soil preparation and conditioner.

Appendix 2-Advanced Bokashi Production

Bokashi is the Japanese word for fermented plant matter. There are thousands of types of bokashi for you to make and explore. Once you learn the fundamentals of bokashi production you will find many creative ways to capture seemingly worthless organic materials and turn them into a powerhouse of nutrients and beneficial inoculants for plants and livestock.

Fertilizer production is a very complex procedure. However, with anaerobic composting, it is much simpler once you learn the basic steps. Whether you are going to use on farm or off farm inputs, you can learn to formulate and then calibrate what you are producing for accurate application. This will insure consistent yields. Bokashi (fermented plant matter) as a microbial fertilizer and worm multiplier works well in our Vermiculture also.

Effective microorganisms ferment rice bran, copra meal and carbonized rice hull, making it a powerful fertilizer rich in microbial activity. It inoculates the soil with beneficial microorganisms, adds organic matter and feeds earthworms, helping them to breed and populate depleted soils. We use a minimum of three substrates to give a diverse and balanced diet to the microbes. The copra meal is sometimes substituted with cow manure depending on availability. It is a flexible formula because the EM adapts to a wide range of ingredients. It's economical because it will replace chemical fertilizers and utilize waste materials that are inexpensive or free.

ALOHA "all around" Bokashi

People always ask for our secret mix, so here it is:
- 3 sacks Magaspang [D3] - about 100 Kilos
- 3 sacks Rice Hull Charcoal (Carbonized [D4]) ~100 Kilos
- 1 sack Copra Meal - 50 Kilos
- 200ml. EM and 200 ml. molasses diluted in 20 Liters water

Mix it just like cement on concrete floors; the bulk dry ingredients first, and then add EM solution. We ferment this mixture for two weeks in a sealed drum. Fills three 160-Liter containers.

There are cheaper formulas; some use only rice bran, but few can rival the performance of this three-ingredient recipe. Remember, the more diverse the ingredients, the more effective the fermentation and fertilizer will be in propagating the beneficial bacteria and fungi.

Substitution List

Review Chapter 10 on composting and C/N ratios. You can bokashi anything that will balance out to 30:1. A range from 20:1 to 40:1 is acceptable.

Possible Substitutes relative to C/N Ratios

1st Choice	2nd Choice	3rd Choice	4th Choice
Chopped straw	Wheat Straw	Rice Straw	Corn Husks
Fishmeal	Blood meal	Soy meal	
Cow Manure	Kitchen Waste		
Hog Manure	Chicken manure		
Bone meal	Eggshells		
Wheat mill cleanings	Wheat Bran	Rice Bran	
Saw Dust	Rice Hull		
Coffee bean sludge	Potato waste		
Sugar cane scrap	Pineapple waste	Baggasse	Molasses

Strange Things We Have Fermented (From Drugman Drug House- a drug store on our island that donates their damaged goods)

Soured milk powder-high in protein with sugars from lactose. We added rice bran, charcoal and sawdust with a little copra meal to bring up the nitrogen level.

Stale biscuits-carbohydrates with refined sugar. We mixed in our standard copra meal bokashi and added extra EME.

Spoiled Soy Meal- mixed with high carbon ingredients from the rice mill-rice bran (D3) and rice hull (D4) and charcoalized rice hull.

C.R.H. Carbonized rice hull is put to good use in our classic bokashi recipe. It is a harboring agent for microorganisms and conditions the soil. It allows our radish and carrots to penetrate the clay soil we grow in.

We have found that we get the best fermentation from bokashi made with 3 or more different ingredients. It is more conducive to the process. The more diverse the ingredients, the more stable and productive the fermentative by-products become. Biodiversity is an important aspect to stability; it will bring in richness and balance similar to natural systems like those found on the forest floor. We always use at least 2 carbon sources and sometimes as many as 3 nitrogen sources. This bio-diversity will be highly effective in the soil or as a compost facilitator. We use a 3-ingredient bokashi recipe for fermenting our kitchen waste. It is available to the community. There are people in this city growing healthy plants for food production or landscaping out of their garbage. Bokashi is simple to use and easy to make. Just keep the components diverse when you make it and you will see great results. The purpose of bokashi is two-fold; you are improving soil structure and nutrients within the soil as well as inoculating a high level of beneficial microorganisms into the soil. These are the workers that further dismantle the substrates that turn it into fertilizer for your plants.

Radish and carrot can grow straight in clay soil if the soil is prepped with bokashi and carbonized rice hull. Heavy mulch makes them sweet.

Aerated Compost Tea (A.C.T.) Brewer- Compost is constantly circulated in this brewer, preventing pockets of sediment and stagnation. The air stones are set in the bottom of the side chambers and the air brings water up the chamber. Then it is sucked down a swirling vortex in the center of the inverted water jug and re-circulates through the chambers again and again.

Appendix 3- Foliar Fertilizers/Sprays

With all the instant gratification available to the consumer these days, nature seems to take a long time. Stabilizing your soil, pasture and livestock areas don't happen over night. Nevertheless, Microbial Management with foliar sprays and fertilizers can help in the transition.

There is now a Japanese technology available that uses beneficial microorganisms for soil preparation, composting, disease and pest management. We use EM1 (Effective Micro-organisms) to make Fermented Plant Extracts, FPE, from marigold, oregano, lemon grass, weeds, etc. This multiplies phototropic bacteria species and is sprayed to enhance plant growth and disease resistance.

EM is used to ferment neem leaves, garlic, ginger, etc. as a bio-pesticide called EM5. It is mixed 1:250 with water and used as a foliar spray. On soil, we use fermented garbage juice, fermented rice wash, vermicompost tea, bokashi tea and aerobic compost tea as well as fish silage or FAA [fish amino acid]. Until our soil is perfect we find foliar feeding a great help in fertilizing the plant. However, it is our goal to feed the plant through the soil as we pioneer this high acid, clay soil grassland into healthy farmland.

The following preparations are utilized at Aloha House, with the exception of liquid manure. The techniques are gleaned from Japanese, Korean, Thai, German and American methods. Each of them has their own devotees. Liquid manure is not recommended for food production, due to surviving pathogens. I include it here because of its popularity as promoted in *Ten Acres Enough*.

We have learned to use some of the best concoctions available from a broad spectrum of influences as diverse as Bio-dynamics, ACT,

Kyusei Nature Farming and Korean Natural Farming. While feeding the soil is the primary means of natural fertilization, in transition years feeding the plant through the stomata will help when compost reserves are not sufficient. These are temporary means used for adjusting fertility shortcomings due to oversights of the farmer, lack of organic matter or compost shortages. Some of these problems are due to initial land preparation in the early years where forecasting is inaccurate due to little available data. These are palliatives that should not be necessary on established soils in subsequent years, when a climax vegetative state is reached.

For Vegetative Stage when Nitrogen needs are higher

Name	Fish Silage, Fish Emulsion, F.A.A. (fish amino acid)
Formula	Equal parts by weight Fish scraps or fish meal with molasses and water. Dissolve molasses in water first, ferment Anaerobically
Substitutions	Cuddle fish trimmings, marine waste
Time	10 days
Usage	Dilute and spray 1:100 as foliar fertilizer, soil treatment, compost activator

Sprayed in the growth stage of the plant, this high nitrogen formula helps develop a lush canopy. It is used on new soil when sugar cane is planted. Corn usually follows peanuts and does well with our ordinary composts, but the first year of converting new soil, we need FAA to meet the nitrogen need.

Each table gives you an idea on how to get started. Make sure you do your homework and study all the possibilities. I've compiled a list of useful links in appendix 6 at the end of this book. Each concoction is listed with alternate names, the formula for mixing, substitutions for items you may not have access to, the time required for the process, and ways to dilute and/or spray as a foliar fertilizer.

For Flowering Stage

Name	Foliar Calcium
Formula	Cleaned chicken eggshells are burnt over a fire or broiled in an oven till black, then steeped in natural vinegar. Use 2.5 liters of vinegar per one kilo of burnt eggshells.
Substitutions	Duck eggs, ostrich eggs, etc.
Time	20 days
Usage	Flower setting, eliminates blossom end rot in tomatoes, Dilute 1:100

Foliar Calcium is excellent at preventing blossom end rot in tomatoes and will help plants to flower in season. The calcium helps with flower setting; it prevents the blossom from falling off prematurely so fruits can start to form.

This is the motor and pump behind the pressure sprayer that gives you the *power* to inoculate at high levels with the least amount of effort. Keep your sprayer pressure below 10 bars. When the pressure is too high it will inhibit the microorganisms.

Instead of using chemicals to induce flowering, growers can extract natural calcium from burnt eggshells using vinegar.

For Fruit Setting

Name	Calcium Phosphate
Formula	Cleaned cow bones are burnt over a fire or broiled in an oven till black, then steeped in natural vinegar. Use 2.5 liters of vinegar per one kilo of burnt bones.
Substitutions	Cow, goat, fish bones
Time	30 days
Usage	Fruit Setting-Dilute 1:100

Calcium Phosphate is used on fruit trees and vegetable crops when the available calcium and phosphate is low. It helps in fruit setting so that after flowers form and start fruiting, the young fruits do not as readily abort.

Soil Nutrients

Name	FGJ-Fermented Garbage Juice
Formula	Harvest from anaerobic fermentation of kitchen garbage
Time	Harvested daily from drip fermentor
Usage	Leachate is for soil treatment and not a good foliar spray Dilute 1:100

Some kitchen compost containers have drains to allow the liquid to be extracted during fermentation. This makes for a nutritious soil drench but should not be sprayed. It could spread pathogens if not fully fermented and cleared of risks.

Old School

Name	Liquid manure, manure tea
Formula	Steep manure in a sack into water drum, CAUTION- Can spread pathogens
Time	Up to 2 weeks
Usage	Not recommended, due to surviving pathogens

This old school technique has helped many farmers out of a nutrient crisis, but it comes with considerable risk. The raw manure can pass on pathogens and putrefaction is a common result of feces soaked in water. **WE ADVISE AGAINST THIS TECHNIQUE** but include it here because of the influence the excellent book <u>10 Acres Enough</u> has had in certain circles.

Liquid Extracts

Name	Bokashi Liquid Extract
Formula	Steep bokashi in a sack into water drum and aerate mixture
Time	24 hours
Usage	Beneficial microbes exclude pathogens

Rich in EM power, this concoction will boost the immune system of certain plants and add nutrients through the stomata. This is a foliar fertilizer that is dependant on the quality of the compost.

EM-5 Foliar Spray

Names	EM5-Biorepelent
Formula	Steep high antioxidant herbs and plants with EM and Molasses and vinegar and alcohol
Substitutions	Chili, radish, neem, garlic, marigold etc
Time	14 days
Usage	Dilute 1:250

Prepare 2 parts chopped greens from neem leaves or use seeds or oil extracts, and radish roots, garlic, ginger and aloe Vera. Mix with 5 parts water, 1 part EM1, 1 part Molasses, 1 part unpasteurized natural vinegar like tuba, and 1 part low-grade alcohol. Stir daily to prevent gasses from building up on the surface of ingredients. We spray this mixed together with FPE in weekly applications.

EM treated waste water from rinsing rice will help fertilize as a soil drench and will also remediate the canal if you pour it into the system.

Recycle Your Kitchen Waste and Prevent Red Tide

Name	Fermented Rice Wash, FRW
Formula	Add 5ml Molasses/5ml EM/1 liter wash from rice
Substitutions	Mong bean wash, Cassava wash, potato starch water, fish cleaning water, etc.
Time	7 days fermentation-stores 1 more week only
Usage	Dilute 1:500 for plant spray, 1:100 for kitchen and bathroom use, replace ½ soap for non-whites

This liquid must be used in 1-2 weeks. It is less stable than other brews because of starches. It works in compost very well. We use it in our septic tanks and pour it down drains. It prevents red tide in the sea so we use it in canals. It also works well in reducing soap use. Add it to your non-white laundry.

A.C.T.

Name	Compost tea, Aerated compost tea-ACT
Formula	Steep mature compost in a water drum or pail with an aquarium aerator to grow beneficial microorganisms. We pump 21 Liters of air per minute for 30 liters of water containing 1-2 liters of compost. We feed the microbes by adding 200 ml. molasses and 100 ml. FAA, 1 T sea salt/lime
Time	12-36 hours
Usage	Dilute 1:2-5 for foliar spray or soil drench

ACT- Aerated Compost Tea is very nutritious for plants if the compost is of high quality. Short brew cycles of 12-18 hours can produce high quantities of beneficial bacteria for vegetable production. Longer brew cycles are necessary for fungal growth, needed for perennials, orchards and timber trees.

This is the swirling vortex that draws the compost down as the side columns pump water through an air drive system. This prevents the compost from stagnating or putrefying on the bottom. A high level of oxygen is reached through the air compressor's continual pumping of air throughout the system.

The 4 way coupling is converted to a 6 way coupling. This makes it easy to harvest our tea and clean the brewer. The air moves the water in a vortex. It empties into a 20-liter pail (5-gallon) below. This one is made with a 20-liter (5 gallon) water jug and actually makes 30 liters (7 gallons) because of the capacity in the PVC columns that circulate air.

Aloha's Favorite Tea- Vermicast tea

Names	**Vermicast tea**, vermi-tea, Vermicompost tea
Formula	Steep finished worm castings in a water pale or drum with an aquarium type aerator to grow beneficial microorganisms. We pump 21 Liters of air per minute for 30 liters of water containing 1-2 liters of compost. We feed the microbes by adding 200 ml. molasses and 100 ml. FAA, 1 T sea salt/lime
Time	12-36 hours
Usage	Dilute 1:2-5 for foliar spray or soil drench

Vermicasts are superior to vermicompost. Use only the best to get the best results. Brew longer to get the fungi levels high for orchards, roses and other perennials. We brew up to 36 hours for our pineapple and pour 1 liter into the soil around each plant.

EM Specialty Sprays

Names	FPE-Fermented Plant Extract
Formula	Steep chopped weeds and local green crops and tree leaves in water with EM and Molasses to broaden the spectrum of beneficial phototropic microorganisms 1:1:30
Substitutions	Stinging Nettle, Comfrey, Marigold, Neem, Papaya, weeds, chives, lemon grass, China berry
Time	14 days
Usage	Dilute 1:250

The plant extracts from Mexican Oregano, marigold, chives, lemon grass and weeds make an outstanding foliar fertilizer and pick up robust colonies of beneficial microorganisms that work to nurture and protect our plants.

Medium Tech – Some equipment is required for brewing compost teas, but it is a good fit for market farmers and growers of premium fruits. The EM technology is low tech, and lower in labor, due to its fermentation process. It is useful to growers that want to minimize their start up costs.

Note the swirling vortex effect that keeps the compost from putrefying on the bottom of the apparatus. It circulates and extracts the nutrients while feeding the microorganisms.

School lectures are a good way to teach the benefits of microorganisms. This school received valuable information that can help them win at the city garden tournament in Puerto Princesa City.

Every spot is utilized in a productive garden. Shade loving flowers and chili peppers are next to a wall and netted from direct sun.

Chubby bananas require nutrient-rich soil prepared for the cultivar we grow.

On farm generated fertility has made our lettuce production very profitable. Our compost is all we need to grow this plant. The raised bed keeps it from water logging during rainy season. The soil preparation is minimal.

Rice paddies are flooded to control weed growth. In a chemical based agricultural model, roots and weeds are cleared and burned, as well as the straw. Soil preparation in this system is the removing of organic matter. In our sustainable practice we add composts, crop residues and mulches. Even weeds can be plowed under as green fertilizer. EM will break the dormancy of weed seeds, so you can plow them under all at once and not battle them continually. We use the weeds as a fertilizer when pioneering soils.

Appendix 4- Soil Preparation

S oil conditions can improve rapidly when the right ingredients are added. You have to learn what to add. The quantities in nutrients run a range of effectiveness from a maximum to a minimum. It's equally important to know how to add your amendments. Lime, Ash and Carbonized Rice Hull (uling) all require soil tests to keep the PH range where it should be. You will develop an eye for it as you see how your plants respond, but a little science never hurts.

Our soil preparation guide was worked out over a period of 3 years. We've maximized the performance for our clay soil in the tropics for growing market vegetables, fruits and cereal crops. We are always learning and finding better ways to fine-tune our system. It is highly experimental, yet reliable enough to see consistent results. Your available inputs, soil type, and composting methods will give you all the feed back you need if you keep good notes. You must have an active eye for what is working and what needs to change.

More O^2 - The Kings of Compost turn another pile to feed the aerobic microbes. This batch has seaweed with cow manure and sawdust. We like to turn it 3 times, preferably every 5 days then let it mature after the third turning for 2-9 months.

The broad fork aerates soil. Properly aerated soil will produce a bountiful harvest year-round in the tropics.

Before- acidic clay soil, low organic matter

After - The same area after 3 years of compost and crop rotations that built up the soil. Flexible planning helped us adjust to our learning process. Information gathering is ongoing.

New Soil Preparation

1. Clear grass and weeds for compost
2. Plow or spade down to subsoil (1st dig)
3. Spade in rice hull and charcoal (double dig)
4. Spade in Compost, bokashi etc.
5. Spade in all other Amendments
6. Aerate with Broad Fork
7. Water in
8. Mulch
9. Water in
10. Place irrigation lines
11. Water in until soil's moist top to bottom

First Year Amendments: 2-4 times

- 12 -15 pails Compost (4-5 tons/hectare)
- 10 pails Rice Hull
- 1 pail Vermicompost
- 2 pails Bokashi
- 2 pails Ash
- 10L Bat Guano
- 10-20L Lime

> Per 1m X 9 m bed
> (3 ft X 30 ft)
> Pail=20 Liters

Established Soil - 2nd year and after

1. Clear Crop Residue for compost
   (Leave roots)
OR Use as Mulch / Green Fertilizer
2. Aerate with Broad Fork
   (No turning)
3. Add Compost – top dress
4. Add specialty Amendments
   (Crop Specific- surface only)
5. Water in
6. Mulch
7. Water in
8. Place irrigation lines
      Water in until soil's moist top to bottom

Second Year Amendments: 2-4 times

- 10 Pails Compost
- 1 Pail Vermicompost
- 2 Pails Bokashi
- 1 Pail Ash
- 5L Bat Guano
- 1-5 L Lime

Per 1m X 9 m bed
(3 ft X 30 ft)
Pail=20 Liters

Flower setting and Fruit Sweetening

For flower-setting and fruit-sweetening we have come a long way. We are still refining this mix through ongoing experimentation.

<u>Turbo Super Mix</u>

8 pails Cow - manure - seaweed compost
4 pails Aerobic Compost
2 pails Vermicompost
2 pails Bokashi
2 pails Ash
½ pail Bat Guano
<u>½ pail Lime</u>
Yields 3 sacks=use 1 liter per vine

This specialty mix was originally formulated for our off-season watermelon. It seems to hold a dynamic balance for many of our intensive fruit and vegetable vine crops. Measuring by volume works better for us, the 20-liter pail is our standard measuring unit. Apply to mounded soil 1 meter apart two weeks before transplanting. The calcium (lime) is important for carrying all the other trace elements and assisting metabolic processes, even if you are close to your pH goal state, it is needed at optimal levels.

Our off-season watermelon was a great success; we formulated a natural sweetener that kept the phosphates and potassium in balance with the calcium! The Brix meter is helpful in determining a more accurate sugar content in any fruit or vegetable. Naturally grown mango is very sweet.

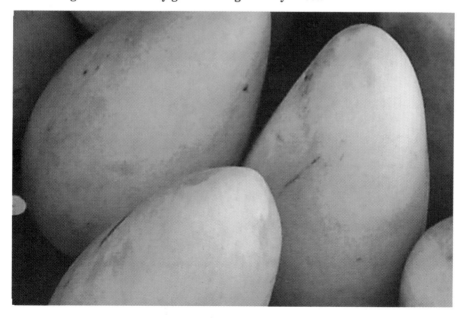

Measured applications and careful note-taking have helped us achieve consistent results. Each amendment we use has to be field-tested due to the variability of the nutrients. Once we regulate our composting and formulate our mixes, we can have a more controlled outcome. This is the hardest part of the technology for chemical farmers to understand. The standard NPK ratings are not as helpful as a careful eye trained to see how your crops respond to your soil management.

Seedling Bag Mix

In the green house we have this starter recipe for our "Poly Bags". We change the quantities of select ingredients depending on the crop. This is still highly experimental. Our green houseplants do well in bags; they're easy to move and utilizes the space well.

Tomato			Bell Pepper	
Vermicast	40	L	Vermicast	40.0 L
Crop Compost	80	L	Seaweed Compost	40.0 L
Charcoal	40	L	Crop Compost	40.0 L
Rice Hull	40	L	Rice Hull	80.0 L
Soil	20	L	Soil	40.0 L
Sand	20	L	Bat Guano	10.0 L
Bat Guano	5	L	Bokashi	5.0 L
Bokashi	5	L		
Lime	5	L		

Makes 10 bags (11X11X18) Or 8 bags (12X12X19)

Aloha House December, 2002- the upper garden

Aloha House September, 2005- the same shot of the upper garden

Fertilization can be supplemented in the green house with soil drenches of compost tea.

All our students leave with a bottle of Effective Microorganisms, a training manual, and 5 bags of organic amendments. They also receive 2 discount "Alumni referral coupons" for 10% off for our Introduction to Sustainable Agriculture seminar. This adds to our word-of-mouth promotion. We only want the growers that will implement this technology; therefore we don't do any advertising.

Appendix 5 – Users' Guide to Aloha Fertilizers

I n our training seminars, every student gets a bottle of EME. We teach them by making it in class. They also are trained on how to use their bag of five different soil amendments. This encourages students to use them in the project that they have already started. Some students are just starting out with a new plot. They really appreciate the fertilizers and are encouraged by the results once their plants start to grow. They can see what is succeeding as they learn how each item performs for their soil.

It is advisable to test your soil to know the

quantity of nutrients that will be required to establish the fertility

needed for your cropping system. Your actual needs will vary considerably from our needs. The recommendations below are merely entry points to build upon. Few farmers ever test their soil, but many have an intuitive feel for the quantities of compost, etc. required because they are good at observing the plants they grow. Some of our students require 2-10 times our quantities, depending on the extent that the soil has been abused or depleted. It is important to start low if you have not tested the soil when using lime and guano, due to the cumulative effect they have over the years.

1. EME - Start Spraying EME 1:1: 500

Example: Backpack sprayer = 30ml EME: 30 molasses: 15 L water

Always use clean water, not city water with chlorine. [You can mix the EME and molasses with water 2-12 hours in advance.]

EME Application: Spray at 100 ml./ sq. meter or 1000 L. / hectare to start. Spray plants, soil, compost etc. One liter EME will dilute and spray ½ hectare = 5,000 sq. Meters.

2. Bokashi

Broadcast as a fertilizer, use for side dressing or bury into soil while plowing. 100g /sq. Meter = 1,000 Kg / hectare = 20 sacks / hectare.

In Kitchen Compost - Use 1 kg. Bokashi /20L kitchen waste

3. Vermicompost

Broadcast as fertilizer or bury into soil while plowing.

100g /sq. Meter = 1,000 Kg / hectare = 20 sacks / hectare. Use in potting soil.

4. Make potting soil

You can give your plants a good start without chemicals or unnatural additives by starting your plants in cups in a nursery. Like children, many plants need a controlled environment to prosper.

Mix:

1-liter vermicasts	1-liter rice hull charcoal
1-liter sand	1-liter ordinary soil
1 small handful bokashi	1 small handful bat guano
1 small handful lime	

Make Soil Blocks- You can give your plants a good start without chemicals or unnatural additives by starting your plants in soil blocks in a nursery. Soil blocks maximize seedling growth by "air pruning"

roots and allowing the quick establishment of the plant. You also avoid transplant stress, as the plant is not disturbed in the rhizosphere by cup removal.

Aloha Block Mix:

- 5 L Rice Hull Charcoal – dry
- 5 L Crop Compost - dry
- 5 L Vermicompost – Moist
- 2½ L Sand – dry
- 2½ L Soil – dry
- 1 L Bat Guano – dry
- 1 L Bokashi
- ½ L Lime – dry
- ½ L Ash – dry
- 200 ml EME plus~ 4 L Water (depends on moisture)

- Yields 16 - 3"X 6" PVC t block cylinders.

If your ingredients are too wet you need to reduce the moisture.

Archie carries a tray for seeding and germination.

The roots are "air pruned" and grow throughout the block, poised to grow into the soil when they are transplanted, and with minor disturbance.

The soil blocker makes four perfect squares every batch. The mix is wetter than normal potting mix so that it binds together. There are all kinds of sizes available.

An inexpensive soil blocker can be made with a 3"- 4" PVC  pipe cut to 12"-18" sections and drilled with small holes to break the suction. A round wooden block tamps the soil so that it holds together. Square blocks are more efficient in space utilization. Rounds waste valuable green house space but still make for better nursery conditions than the plastic cups or trays.

Tomatoes set out and develop quicker when grown in blocks. The roots wind around in a cup and are stressed when planted, but with soil blocks the roots grow out to the edge. The soil blocks also preserve the taproot and allow quick recovery from transplanting.

5. Bat Guano

Use guano directly in the soil 2 weeks prior to sowing or as a basal application. Hand broadcast 1 kilo / 30sq. Meters. Our bat guano is rated at NPK 6-7-2 and is a good source of phosphate and nitrogen. Supplement with potash to bring up the Potassium (K) for a more "complete fertilizer".

It is very useful as a bi-annual or tri-annual mineral fertilizer replacement for phosphate, especially if you cannot get mined organic supplements to replace the values that were removed from harvesting your crops.

Guano comes white, black and brown in Palawan. Different bats and seasons produce different levels of potassium and phosphates. Guano is a South American term that is used of very specific bird droppings. In popular usage it now is used to describe bat manure.

6. Lime

Acidification of tropical soils is a natural result of rainfall, climate and soil management interaction. When chemicals are used it gets worse more rapidly than the natural process. Hydrogen ions are released and immobilize nutrients as the pH drops. Aluminum is then released instead and subsequently poisons the plant.

Use lime by mixing into the soil when preparing beds to balance pH. A soil test will help give you the best results, but you can add at 1 kilo/ 100 sq. meters to start and see how your crops perform. Make sure it is buried and mixed in 10-20 cm. for maximum effects. It is a great source of calcium and will also raise soil pH.

The chart below will give you a rough guide on what to expect, but soil structure, organic content and microbial activity can help or hinder pH shift.

Lime Required in Kilos/sq M for Aloha House

	pH	GOAL
	7.0	6.5
Starting Soil pH	Lime	Required
6.8	0.3	None
6.6	0.8	None
6.4	1.2	1.1
6.2	1.7	1.4
6.0	2.2	1.8
5.8	2.6	2.2
5.6	3.1	2.6
5.4	3.5	3.0
5.2	4.0	3.4
5.0	4.9	3.8
4.8	5.0	4.2

Agricultural Ground Limestone

7. Live Stock Electrolyte Mix

This re-hydrator is used for stressed livestock. When moving animals, they often will experience dehydration. This mix will improve recovery from transporting. It is also helpful when your livestock experience diarrhea or other stressors. Works on humans too! Just be sure to use food grade molasses.

Electrolyte Mix

¼ teaspoon baking soda	¼ teaspoon salt
3 tbsp. molasses	1-Liter Water

After our "weaners" arrive, we give them all they can drink. They are usually stressed from transport. The electrolyte mix can be used in the drinker instead of water if the piglets are trained to use it. They are very smart and can learn in one day if you hand -operate it a few times till they smell the concoction coming out. They like to eat and drink so the drinker has a drain below it. We only use D1 grade rice bran for maximum weight gain.

Appendix 6 – A Rice Mill Primer

T he rice industry in the Philippines has gone through various challenges and will benefit from EM technologies. Growing, harvesting and processing rice creates high volumes of waste that can be captured and converted back into fertilizer for the next crop. It is important to understand the various grades and different types of mills for rice. The waste from small mills is different than the waste from the larger mills. To keep costs down we want the best value for the money we are spending. We use different grades of rice mill by-products depending on the availability from the mill in our area. We never use the expensive grades for fertilizers. We always try to get the best grades; the higher protein will pay off in weight gain and genetic maximums.

Rice Mill By-Products

Grade	Common Name	Filipino	Waste Source	Carbon/Nitrogen
[D4]	Rice Hull	Ipa, Labhang	From Dehusking	high carbon
[D3]	Crushed Rice Hull	Magaspang	from beltway	high carbon/ some nitrogen
[D2]	Rice Bran	Darak	from cleaning	lower carbon/ higher nitrogen
[D1]	Rice Bran	Tiki-Tiki	from polishing	low carbon/ high nitrogen

Notice that the names vary from region to region and country to country. If we use the grade ranking we will avoid much confusion. D4, rice hull, is excellent for making charcoal. This is a good soil conditioner and used in our bokashi also. The carbon bond is weakened in the charcoal process and will not tie up as much nitrogen when added to the soil. However, it makes a good home for the microbes. The charcoal works as a harboring agent for the beneficial microbes in the soil or in the intestines of livestock. That's right, we add charcoal at 0.5% to our formulated feed to enhance digestion and help the EM work as a pro-biotic.

We use the D3 as a bokashi ingredient. When it is not available we use D4 and extra nitrogen in the form of copra meal or manure. As a feed ingredient it will not help your goats grow or fatten your hogs. The crude protein is very low. However, it is inexpensive and makes for good fertilizer. On our island we have to be flexible and keep looking for alternatives.

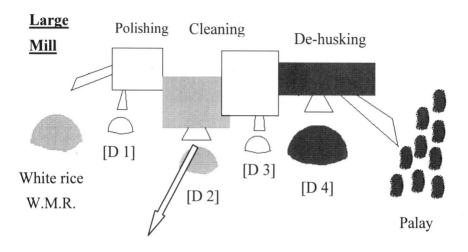

Large Mill

Polishing   Cleaning   De-husking

[D 1]

White rice
W.M.R.

[D 3]

[D 2]   [D 4]

Palay

Unpolished rice

The large rice mill gives you differing grades of rice bran. Don't use the D2 for fattening if you can get the D1. It is superior in quality and nutrients to [D3] darak.

The advantage of the large mill is a greater variety of by-products. When rice is consumed unpolished the humans benefit from the vitamins, minerals and fiber. By and large, most Filipinos prefer white-well-milled-polished-rice. Which means we feed the best parts to livestock and suffer from various ailments due to the nutritional imbalance of our grains.

The main reason we succeeded in our programs is because we did our homework and secured good suppliers for the materials we needed to produce a high quality bokashi. You can waste a lot of time and money with poor quality feed or weak fertilizers. Take a tour of the mills in your area and try to understand the process so that you can find the best supplier for your needs.

Small Mill

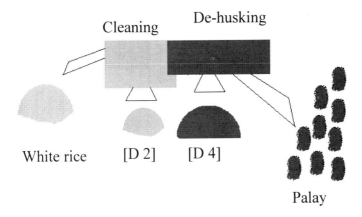

The small mill is more prevalent, but it has it's own challenges. It does not completely polish rice. Therefore, D1 is not available. Only D2 and D4 are separated in this type of mill. It prevents the buyer from benefiting from high protein feed stocks and inexpensive D3 fertilizer components. You must be aware of the shortcomings of this mill and compensate accordingly.

One way to make up for high carbon ingredients is by adding more nitrogen. For feed we use soy meal and copra meal. Fishmeal will taint the flavor of meat and does not command a high price. Our organic free-range meat and poultry products are priced 20%-40% more than the prevailing price because our feed makes the animals taste like wild goat, pig etc. The proper grade bran makes the difference between breaking even and earning high profits.

Remember to plan around the seasons, most large mills shut down when palay is scarce. They need hundreds of sacks of palay to process to make it worthwhile to run. They will run out of rice hull and rice bran for up to 3 months. Prepare for this eventuality by stockpiling for the future needs of your operation.

Appendix 7 – Miscellaneous

T he EM distributor in the Philippines has select dealers for EM products. Aloha House is a dealer and has many other products available for organic farming. Contact us at:

Aloha House
777 Mitra Road
Brgy. Santa Monica
Puerto Princesa City
5300 Palawan

Email: mik@mozcom.com
http://www.alohahouse.org
Follow the links to Sustainable Agriculture

We have on going seminars by appointment for advanced training. We are available to help you with your agricultural training, planning, and development. We have professional consultation services also.

Seed Suppliers

Allied Botanical – (02) 911-0836

East-West Seed Co.- (044) 766-4952 to 57

Harbest Agribusiness Corp.- (02) 671-7411 to 14

Ramgo Seeds- (02) 371-3463

EM and Inoculation Resources:

EMRO

http://www.emro.co.jp/english/

May God bless you on your adventure in agriculture!

Keith Mikkelson

The Aloha House Staff

Conversion of International Measurements

Metric to	Imperial
1 millimeter [mm]	0.03937 in
1 centimeter [cm]	0.3937 in
1 meter [m]	1.0936 yd
1 kilometer [km]	0.6214 mile
1 hectare [ha] =10,000 m^2	2.4711 acres
1 sq km [km^2] =100 ha	0.3861 $mile^2$
1 cu meter [m^3]	1.3080 yd^3
1 liter [l]	1.76 pt
1 gram [g]	0.0353 oz
1 kilogram [kg]	2.2046 lb
1 metric ton [t]	0.9842 ton

Tables and Figures

Glossary

A.C.T.- Aerated compost tea, see compost tea

Acidic- pH below 7.0

Aerobic- A process that uses oxygen, "with air"

Aerobic compost- High quality compost made "with air", turning is required to feed oxygen to thermophilic bacteria that create heat, usually in piles or windrows. Inoculation with the proper beneficial microorganisms is helpful.

Alkaline- pH above 7.0

Amendment- Organic material added to soil to improve structure, drainage or fertility

Anaerobic- A process that does not use oxygen, "without air"

Anaerobic composting- High quality compost made "without air", often called fermentation or silage, usually in drums, pails or plastic wraps. Inoculation with the proper beneficial microorganisms is necessary.

Annual- Plants with a life cycle of 1 season

Beneficial Microorganisms- Small units of life that help things grow or maintain health

Broadcast- Using your hands or machines to distribute seeds or fertilizer over the surface of the soil

China berry- Mistaken for neem, it actually is Melia azedarach

Compost- Organic matter systematically combined to create a fertile end product that builds up soil and feeds plants. Good quality compost is high in beneficial bacteria and fungi and will inoculate your soil and feed your plants.

Compost tea- High quality foliar spray and soil drench made by soaking good compost in water and feeding the bacteria with molasses and fish emulsions. Aeration of quality compost guarantees pathogen free tea. This populates beneficial microorganisms.

Cover crop- Plants that occupy the surface of your planting area.

Crop rotation- The practice of using different plants from the previous to minimize pests and disease.

F.A.A.- Fish amino acid, fish silage and fish emulsion

Faucet- Tap, water source

Fermentation- An anaerobic process to increase the nutrient values of fertilizers, composts and feeds.

Fertilizer- Nutrients added to soil or sprayed on leaves. Nitrogen, phosphorus and potassium are often considered the macronutrients, but calcium, iron, zinc, boron, etc. are also important at varying degrees.

Fish emulsion- Fermented fish waste high in nitrogen

Flemingia- A legume shrub, Flemingia macrophylla

Green fertilizer- Plants grown and hoed or plowed back into the soil to increase the fertility of the next crop. Often legumes.

Green manure- Plants grown and hoed or plowed back into the soil to increase the fertility of the next crop. Often legumes.

Humus- The result of composts, mulches and green manures transforming into a dark, moist, sticky yet crumbly mass in the soil that feeds crops. Clay is necessary to form the humus crumbs that bind the humic acids.

Inoculate- To treat or spray with beneficial microorganisms, usually sprayed on plant surface or added to soil via bokashi and compost.

Intercrop- Plants grown together or simultaneous planting.

Interplant- See intercrop.

Ipil-ipil- Leucaena diversifolia.

Kakawati- A legume tree, Madre de cacao, Gliricidia sepium.

Kang Kong- Morning Glory, *Ipomoea violacea.*

Kudzu- Pueraria phaseoloides.

Lactic acid bacteria- A family of bacteria that break down organic matter and form lactic acid, usually through fermentation.

Manure- Originally meaning that which is added by hand, now commonly understood.

Mesophiles- Aerobic bacteria that operate in temperatures below thermophiles during composting.

Neem tree- Indian neem, *Azadirachta Indica.*

Nitrogen fixation- The process in which air borne nitrogen (N_2) from air in soil is reduced to more usable nitrogen forms.

Organic matter- Previously living material like bark, straw, bones, leaves, weeds or manure.

Pathogen- Disease causing microorganisms.

Perennial peanut- Mani-mani, Arachis pintoi.

Perennial- Plants with a life cycle longer than 1 season.

pH- positive hydrogen ions or H^+, a logarithmic scale from 1 to 14, a pH of 7 is neutral. Most crops due well between 6-7 pH.

Photosynthetic bacteria- A family of bacteria that convert organic matter into compost through anaerobic processes.

Putrefaction- The result of anaerobic pathogenic bacteria that cause disease and foul odors.

Rensonii- A legume shrub, Desmodium rensonii.

Rhizobium- Bacteria which live in legume root nodules and fix nitrogen.

Rhizosphere- the root zone of a plant.

Root nodules- Colonies of bacteria that live mainly on the roots of legumes and fix nitrogen.

Sheet composting- Layers of organic matter composted in the field.

Soil structure- Classification of soil types according to particle size.

Stomata- pores found in great number on the underside of leaves.

Thermophilic bacteria- Heat generating bacteria useful in aerobic composting for transforming organic matter into humus while eliminating disease and killing weed seeds.

Vermicast tea- Aerated worm manure in water to grow bacteria and produce large numbers of beneficial bacteria.

Vermicast- The manure excreted by earthworms. A valuable fertilizer.

Volatilization- Chemical process of changing elements into less stable states, such as nitrogen into ammonia.

Zymogenic- Climax state of soil where the microbial population is preventing disease by feeding the plant a balanced nutrient mix thereby building optimum health in the plant.